M.I.Hummel

M.I.HUMMEL

HUMMEL

the complete
collector's guide
and illustrated
reference

design by John Peace

illustration by Robert Frost

HUMMEL

the complete collector's guide and illustrated reference

BY
ROBERT L. MILLER
AND
ERIC EHRMANN

1979
PORTFOLIO PRESS CORPORATION
Huntington, New York 11743

Let's ramble down a happy path
To a joyful and placid land.
Where childrens' faces and angels' graces
Raise the spirit of man.

We'll smile and laugh
Along the path.
We'll take time for reflection.

A moment seized from daily life.
A worthwhile recollection.

E.W.E.

TABLE OF CONTENTS

CHAPTER 1 BERTA'S CHILDHOOD
Detailing the period from her birth in 1909 to her departure for art school, this chapter includes extensive new material on her early years, including her precocious artistic abilities.

2 THE MUNICH YEARS
Having reached maturity, Berta leaves the rural life for art school in Munich where she excels—finishing first in her class—and makes a momentous personal decision.

3 SISTER MARIA INNOCENTIA
From art school, Berta enters the Franciscan Convent at Siessen. Her artistic efforts receive acclaim. There are significant commissions, and the first "M.I. Hummel" figurines made by W. Goebel are introduced.

4 THE FINAL YEARS
As her talent ascends, her health weakens. Her art helps the Convent exist against Nazi antagonism. But as the war draws to a close, it is too late. Sister Maria Innocentia Hummel dies in 1946.

5 THE NAME LIVES ON
After a wartime slowdown W. Goebel resumed full scale production of "M.I. Hummel" figurines. A veritable collecting craze sweeps Europe, America and other lands as literally millions of persons acquire "M.I. Hummel" figurines.

6 THE COLLECTION
Detailed notes on every figurine ever made. More than 225 color photographs showing every variation and rarity known to exist within the complete collection.

7 HISTORY & EXPLANATION OF MARKS & SYMBOLS
This is the one and only accurate account of all markings ever used on W. Goebel's "M.I. Hummel" figurines. And, also for the first time, every number is tracked down and accounted for. This has never appeared in print before, and will be a valuable reference for collectors, appraisers, auctioneers, and dealers.

8 HOW THE HUMMEL FIGURINES ARE MADE
A behind-the-scenes report on the meticulous way in which each figurine is created, including step-by-step information—with photographs—recorded directly at W. Goebel in West Germany. Additional material covers the colorful history of the porcelain tradition in Bavaria, as well as a look at the company and the castle-filled land where they exist.

INDEX:
Alphabetical Listing of all "M.I. Hummel" art objects. A valuable cross-reference to use alone or in conjunction with the numerical listing appearing on page 38.

PAGE 2

PAGE 10

PAGE 22

PAGE 28

PAGE 35

PAGE 37

PAGE 222

PAGE 232

PAGE 252

INTRODUCTION TO SECOND EDITION

There is tremendous excitement surrounding the introduction of this Second Edition of *The Complete Collector's Guide & Illustrated Reference* to M.I. Hummel works of art. The reason is that this volume is not simply an updating of the first edition but rather is the culmination of extensive new research and discoveries occuring since the first edition appeared in 1976.

The Second Edition combines the extensive biographical research and writing of author Eric Ehrmann with the newly completed work of author Robert L. Miller, generally recognized as the world's leading collector and authority on M.I. Hummel figurines. Miller, together with his wife Ruth, has been instrumental in the discovery of many previously unknown figurines.

Extensive travel throughout the United States, Europe and elsewhere has enabled the Millers to piece together many of the puzzles surrounding the history of several rare pieces. All of the Miller's scholarship is included in this volume, together with more than 220 new color photographs depicting virtually every important variation and rarity known to exist. The result is a book of significant new information that will delight collectors everywhere.

Robert Campbell Rowe

Robert Campbell Rowe
Portfolio Press, Huntington, New York
March 1979

CHAPTER I: BERTA'S CHILDHOOD

Illustration of a young girl by
Sister Maria Innocentia Hummel.

Deep in Lower Bavaria where the rolling farmland gives way to the foothills of the Alps, a legend exists about the *Schauerfreitag*, the Friday-born child. According to this bit of ancient folklore, those born on Friday are often gifted with vivid imaginations. They rarely occupy themselves with day-to-day chores. They are different. Berta Hummel was a Friday-born child.

On a cold, drizzly spring day in 1975 in the Bavarian village of Massing an der Rott Berta Hummel's mother, Viktoria, proudly reminisced about her daughter's early childhood in those distant years prior to World War I. "By the time Berta was three, we knew she was an exceptionally gifted child. She would often sit by the light of a window with a pencil in her hand, daydreaming and scribbling." The mother, then on the eve of her ninetieth birthday, sat erect and without a trace of infirmity, her dark eyes twinkling behind wire-rim glasses. The walls were covered with paintings and the family albums bulged with sketches, small drawings, and photographs of the artistic Berta.

In the spacious hallways of the house are carefully arranged cases containing the charming children-dominated figurines that were created from the famous drawings done by Berta in her artistic prime, when she served as the Franciscan nun, Sister Maria Innocentia Hummel.

Berta was born on May 21, 1909, the third daughter of Adolf and Viktoria Hummel. Like all of her brothers and sisters, Berta was born in the three-story stuccoed concrete building that has housed both family and business through four generations. The scalloped Italian facade and the simple sign, "J. Hummel," remain just as they appeared in the years of Berta's childhood. Today, ready-to-wear clothing has replaced dry goods as the essential part of the family's store.

Berta Hummel's mother recalled vividly the era more than sixty years ago when her daughter was born. Her husband ran the family business, dealing with farmers who came to the tiny hamlet for each week's open market. "As a youth, Adolf always wanted to become an artist," said Viktoria Hummel, "but since he was an only son, it was his duty to carry on in his father's footsteps. He spent a great deal of his spare time making woodcarvings and woodcuts, but it was only a hobby."

Berta turned five in 1914, on the eve of the First World War. At that time life in Massing, like that of most rural Bavarian towns, revolved around a strong family alliance and the Roman Catholic church. The Hummel household was no different. Adolf Hummel's modest success in business enabled Viktoria to hire a live in cook-housekeeper to ease the burden of raising the children, but it did not keep seven-year-old Katje and six-year-old Vicki from performing such daily chores as sweeping, beating rugs, washing windows, or gardening. Berta, as her mother recalled, was quite different.

"If she wasn't using wastepaper from the store downstairs to make her drawings, she would be looking for old scraps of cloth to make dolls clothes. Often Lisa, our cook, would help her sew little costumes for the dolls. They were simple, but very colorful. When they finished Berta would go out into the garden or into the kitchen or wherever her two older sisters happened to be busy and put on a little show with the dolls to entertain them." Berta was living up to the nickname her mother had given her, *Das Hummele*, the German word for bumblebee, buzzing from one idea to another. On later occasions, Berta would employ her brother Ady, dressing him in anything from her mother's shawl to a bedsheet to fabricate a makeshift knight's costume or some other outfit that fit one of the various heroes of German folklore, in order to perform spontaneous pantomimes after dinner in front of the family.

These *Märchen* (folk tales) served to pass on the local folklore in an imaginative manner during the days when creative kindergartens and television were part of the distant and unknown future. "The little shows always made my father happy," Berta's brother Adolf remembered, "and he didn't seem to mind that Berta was different from the rest of us when it came to responsibilities around the house. Mind you, she was no favorite, but *Vati* (father) always wanted someone in the family to become an artist, so he let her do as she pleased."

War broke out on July 23, 1914, and within a few months Adolf Hummel was conscripted into the Kaiser's army. Viktoria Hummel then had to preside over the family business and raise the children, who with the birth of Franz on September 15, 1914, numbered six. With the war came food shortages, and the Hummel family, having a better-than-average position in the town of Massing, opened its doors to those neighbors and townfolk who were less fortunate. The diversity of Berta's playmates rapidly increased from a sphere that consisted of her brothers and sisters to a group of children she had previously seen only at Sunday church or Saturday market. Often Frau Hummel would invite these children for Sunday dinner, and give them small gifts they could not afford to buy at the dry-goods store.

"*Mutti* (mother) would give the little girls hair ribbons or kerchiefs and the boys would get pocket combs or new collars to wear with their Sunday shirts to church," Adolf reminisced. "And always afterward, Berta would put on a little show. Not only were these playmates her friends, but her best audience as well."

One of her most famous plays, according to her mother, was done at the age of six—her interpretation of the Grimm fairy tale *Hansel and Gretel*. "Later in her life, Berta's sketches of Hansel and Gretel were made into figurines," Frau Hummel said. "She liked to perform outdoors best, and every Sunday during those springs and summers our backyard was so crowded that Berta began charging admission!"

Of course this admission was not money, it was anything the youngsters could find in the way of clothing or props to keep Berta Hummel's Sunday performances going and producing new shows. And the humble star of the show was always the young, buzzing little *Hummele*. Even the mothers of the children began coming to the Hummel theatre.

In 1917, when she was eight years old, Berta Hummel gave a performance of the *Märchen, Die Hexe* (the sorcerer), but there was little magic a young girl could brew to change the tide of sadness that crept in around her townspeople as the news from the front lines began to indicate that her nation was losing a very costly and embittered war. "Berta always read the letters her father sent us from his unit," Frau Hummel said. "Sometimes he would begin writing and have to stop in the middle of his letter because of the shelling. After reading mail like this, Berta would try to do things to make him happy. She made colorful postcards and illustrated the borders of the letters we sent. Her father always encouraged her to continue with her art, and it was sad for Berta that he could not be at home during these years to guide her."

Shortly after her sixth birthday, Berta entered school. The very strict educational traditions of Prussian-dominated imperial Germany that were developed during the era of Bismarck had filtered down into Bavaria as well, with the exception that the church, rather than the state administered many of the local small-town schools. The *Volksschule* (people's school) in Massing, run by the Sisters of Notre Dame, was such a school. Similar in curricula to the old schoolhouses of American frontier days, it had only two levels, with children between the ages of six and fifteen sitting in the same class, having to listen to their classmates recite daily lessons from books resembling *McGuffey's Eclectic Reader*.

"Berta," her mother said, "spent more time drawing than paying attention to what was going on in class." But the sisters who ran the *Volksschule* in Massing were blessed with the gift of patience, for they knew that their students, coming from poor or modest families, were like the large majority of the young people in Germany who had no chance of advancing to the prestigious *Gymnasium* (college prep school) that would enable them to pursue a university education. They were destined to either return to their family farms or businesses, or possibly to learn a trade.

According to her mother, Berta suffered from the absence of her father during these war years. Her lack of discipline was often disguised by her budding talent and amiable disposition, but when the school sisters of Massing tried to indoctrinate her to the disciplined ways of school life, she had ways of retaliating. She would always try to be the center of attraction in the classroom, just as she had been at home, passing around her drawings or making witty comments that had nothing at all to do with the lessons. When her name was put on the blackboard to stay after classes for insubordination she would erase it during a recess. When the school sisters tried to counsel her, she became coy and uncommunicative.

Frau Hummel was called to the school for a conference regarding Berta's attitude and general lack of bearing. "The sisters asked us to be vigilant at home and even to use force in disciplining Berta," Viktoria Hummel said. "But she was not the same at home as she was at school. How could Adolf be violent with her after going through a war like that?"

After the First World War, the free state of Bavaria was suffering from defeat and chaos like the rest of Germany. Skyrocketing inflation took hold of the economy after King Ludwig III, the constitutional monarch, was deposed by a socialist-communist coup in Munich on the night of November 7, 1918, four days prior to the signing of the Armistice. The socialist-communist coalition leader, Eisner, threatened the farmers with collectivization of their lands, and the businesses and factories with expropriation until his assassination on February 21, 1919. In reaction, communist workers descended upon Munich and the city was besieged with rioting and looting in the streets. The *Landtag* (state house of representatives) was closed on August 12, 1919, and the Bavarian Constitution was absolved. It was under this backdrop of uncertainty that Adolf Hummel tried to reconstruct his business and his role as father after returning from the costly war.

Drawing by Sister M. I. Hummel that is the basis for figurine model HUM 21 "Heavenly Angel."

When Frau Hummel made her visit to the *Volksschule* in Massing to discuss the classroom behavior and work habits of Berta, she asked the sisters to be understanding in light of the times and to discontinue their idea of imposing "hickory stick" punishment on her daughter. "We were lucky," she remembered, "because there was one school sister, Sister Theresa, who recognized Berta's talents as a budding artist and praised her in front of the others who wanted to discipline her." Under the watchful eye of Sister Theresa, Berta Hummel was promoted to the fourth or final form of the Massing *Volksschule.* With a good recommendation from Sister Theresa, Berta was admitted to the *Institut der Englischen Fräulein* (Institute of English Sisters), a prestigious boarding school at Simbach, some twenty miles east of Massing on the Inn River.

The Institute, which stands on a bluff high above the town, is known to local townspeople as *Marienhohe.* Today, the great view from *Marienhohe* across the Inn River, which forms Germany's natural boundary with Austria, is partially blocked by new housing developments, apartment buildings, and small factories. But in 1921, when Berta Hummel matriculated at the school, there was nothing to obstruct the imagination of a young *Schauerfreitag* as she rambled in the lush meadows, looking for wild flowers to brighten her dormitory room during her first days away from home.

If life at Simbach was going to be rewarding for Berta Hummel, she would have to crack the books as well as sketch or go exploring in the fields. As a result of her inattentiveness to the traditional subjects taught at the *Volksschule* in Massing, she was actually one year older than the rest of her classmates. Still, her art pulled her through Simbach. Tutoring succeeded in drawing Berta equal with her classmates and she was

allowed to skip the remainder of her first year a few months after she entered the school, resuming a normal cycle of academic progress.

The Institute had an art department and for the first time Berta Hummel found herself in an academic atmosphere which was able to give direction to the graphic talent she acquired almost instinctively as a young child. During her Simbach years she became a teen-ager. Under the direction of excellent teachers, her artistic energies were channeled into projects which benefited the entire school. She designed scenery and costumes for the school plays, much in the same way she had in her backyard theatre at home in Massing; but instead of the audience being a handful of local children, it was several hundred students, faculty members, and parents in the auditorium of the institution.

The Simbach years were also the years in which Berta Hummel first became interested in watercolors, using them in her earliest attempts at painting landscapes. Her art class would frequently go on nature walks across the border into Austria, or take weekend tours into the Upper Bavarian Alps. She would also spend summers at the home of her great aunt in the alpine town of Berchtesgaden. "Berta would sketch and paint the mountain scenery for hours," her mother reminisced. "Both her father and I began to sense a change that first summer after she entered Simbach. She was doing much more than sketches of her classmates and the little fantasies that used to take place around the house. The progress made her father very proud."

By her fourth year at Simbach, 1925, Berta had branched out into other areas of self-expression. She commenced working with terra cotta clay, sculpting animals and

faces. She also began using her imagination to create pen and ink illustrations of the famous German fairy tale characters that she had discovered back home in Massing at an earlier age and which had served as the subject matter of her backyard theatre plays. These included *Hansel and Gretel* from the Brothers Grimm collection and Weber's *Dreizehn Linden* (Thirteen Tales).

Her illustrations of the Weber tales, which draw their roots from the epic folklore surrounding the Germanic gods, rest today in the archives of the Institute at Simbach. These first attempts of a sixteen-year-old girl, who as a daydreaming child had earned the nickname *Schauerfreitag,* are in the same tradition of the fairy tale characters and feelings she illuminated. A short decade later, her sketches as Sister Maria Innocentia Hummel would be translated into ceramics by W. Goebel as "M.I. Hummel" figurines.

Life at Simbach had been demanding for Berta Hummel, but at the same time it proved to be the right atmosphere for her adolescent years. There were daily wake-ups at five a.m. followed by mandatory morning Mass. Also part of the curriculum were required courses in catechism and the history of the Catholic church. "Berta began learning politeness and how to respect others, as well as the lyceum subjects," her mother recalled. "She began coming home with religious anecdotes and biblical tales instead of the fairy tales that amused her so much when she was home." The spartan religious environment had become an important part of her life, weaving itself into the fibre of her existence to establish a fabric of maturity and strength.

At the Massing *Volksschule,* Sister Theresa had gone to bat for her in front of a faculty irritated by her antics. Now at Simbach there was Sister Stephania, the art professor, who took Berta under her wing, giving guidance and insight to a talented pupil who preferred to communicate with the silence of a sketch instead of the sound of words. "Berta would bring her work home when she came for a weekend or a holiday," her mother remembered. "She was painting still lifes, nature scenes, and of course continuing her little sketches on postcards. My husband began noticing refinement in her style, a self-confidence that let him know Berta really wanted to fulfill his ambition by becoming the family artist."

During her final year at Simbach, Berta began assisting Sister Stephania in the teaching of her elementary art class. She was cooperating with them and helping her sister students as well. Sister Stephania encouraged Berta to continue her art education after graduating from Simbach, with the hope that the *Hummele* would become an art teacher like herself. She counseled Adolf and Viktoria Hummel about their daughter's future, emphasizing the difficulty of becoming a recognized artist during the depressed decade that followed World War I.

Sister Stephania suggested to Adolf and Viktoria Hummel that their daughter continue her education by taking the curriculum for art teachers at the Academy of Applied Arts in Munich. She wrote an excellent recommendation on behalf of her favorite pupil. "Berta would have plenty of time to live the life of a young artist," her mother said, "but she would also be gaining the security of having a profession. Education was not cheap in those days either, especially considering the terrible inflation. We had put Katje and Vicki through girls' school at Simbach and Adolf was attending the boys' school there at the same time as Berta. Centa and Franzl would soon be ready for Simbach, too. The extra money we needed to send Berta to Munich was a sacrifice for the whole family, but it was well worth the joy it gave my husband when he read her letters and saw the illustrations and paintings she brought home over the holidays."

The postwar inflation had indeed hit Massing just as hard as it had Berlin or Munich or Dresden, the loosely knit economies of the small rural towns finding no shelter from the constant erosion of the value of the German currency. In the family library of the

Hummel home in Massing, a chart of the incredible decline in worth of the old German *Reichsmark* is displayed to invited visitors as a grim reminder of those lean days. "In 1924 it took three million of those old *Reichsmarks* to buy one kilo (2¼ lbs.) of black bread," Berta's brother Adolf recalled. "My mother used to ask me to fill a washtub with money when she wanted to go to the bakery. When we wanted to buy pastries or chocolate for Sundays or holidays I had to fill two."

Herr Hummel was a wise businessman and held a privileged place in the Massing infrastructure, earning an income which, even in those hard times, was able to send his children to a private boarding school. His kind heart saw him extending credit to many of his customers, often taking large quantities of farm products in barter or cattle or horses he did not need as payment for past-due accounts. Sometimes, when he had taken in an overabundance of perishables, Frau Hummel would run the egg and vegetable stand on market days just to sell off everything her husband had taken in on trade. "Many times," she recalled, "I remember giving food away. The war had done something to my husband's soul. His heart was with the family, but not with the business. This is why he was so proud that Berta could experience a different kind of life by studying in Munich."

CHAPTER 2: THE MUNICH YEARS

In the fall of 1927, Adolf Hummel took a few days off from his business to accompany his daughter Berta to Munich, making the fifty-mile journey by train. "When he came back he felt just like a schoolboy," Centa Hummel, Berta's youngest sister, said. "He looked renewed, mainly because Berta was following his own childhood ambition."

Centa Hummel closely resembles her late sister. Living in the city of Passau, where the rivers Inn and Donau converge at the Austrian border to form the greater Danube, she teaches applied gymnastics at a private girls' school. In her home hang several Hummel paintings and icons, as well as an oil portrait of her done by her sister, all of which were done after Berta entered the Franciscan Convent at Seissen.

"When Berta first arrived in Munich, she and our father went around looking for a student room that would meet his specifications," Centa said. "They found a pension near the Convent and Church of Saint Ann. That's where she spent her first few months. She would write home that she was very lonely and that the other students who rented rooms at the pension were not too friendly. It was her first experience away from the religious school dormitory, and the life of a big-city student seemed quite foreign to her. Shortly afterward, she moved into a religious dormitory run by the order of the Holy Family in the Blumenstrasse, which offered an environment very much like that of Simbach. Everyone was very serious and the rules were very strict. "When I first went to Munich to study," said Centa, "I followed Berta's example and roomed there. But for me there was too much discipline, so I moved into a small apartment with a school friend."

During the late 1920s, the *Akademie für Angewandte Kunst* was one of the major innovational centers of design and applied arts in Germany. It trained students who wished to become art teachers and those who desired to apply their skills practically in industry or on their own. Specific paths of study were offered in textile weaving and design, book printing and binding, ceramics, sculpture, graphic design, glass blowing, architecture, and in the manufacture and cutting of crystal.

The Academy was directed by Professor Carlo Sattler, an architect and ceramic artist. Sattler was a friend of the American banker James Loeb, a patron of the arts and universities in his ancestral home of Munich as well as in the United States. Along with several of his professors, Sattler was a member of the *Deutsche Werkbund*—a professional association of teachers, artists, designers, and architects who had a great influence on the applied arts and on their institutions of learning. The influence of the *Werkbund* filtered down to the students at the academy, where ripe young minds welcomed fresh ideas with the hope of painting a brighter picture of the world than the sad drudgery of a nation trying to struggle to its feet after losing a war.

"*Werkbund* was the most important movement in art and design that came out of southern Germany, starting about 1910," according to Otto Hufnagel, a former classmate of Berta Hummel at the Munich Academy. "It followed the *Jugendstil* period, coming into public and critical attention at least ten years before the rival *Bauhaus*

The Munich Academy of Applied Arts at Richard Wagnerstrasse 10, circa 1931. The building is now the Paleontological Institute of Munich University.

movement began in Weimar, an historic town in the heart of Germany. Munich, being a predominantly Catholic city, was the logical center for such a movement since religious art and church design had given the city its particular ambience. But there were also groups of *Werkbund* artists, designers, and students in Vienna and Zurich."

The main thrust of the *Werkbund* movement was an attempt to build upon the great artistic traditions of the Baroque and Florentine periods, incorporating these styles into contemporary design concepts. A few years after the end of the First World War, the *Bauhaus* school of design—in direct opposition to the curved, flowing lines of *Werkbund*—began receiving critical attention. "*Werkbund* was a spirit," Hufnagel, who today is the director of the Bavarian State School for Ceramics in Landshut, added. "*Bauhaus* was straight sharp lines, very Protestant in its following, and very much a symbol of the north. We were the south."

Later in her life, Berta Hummel painted icons, murals, and religious frescoes using Baroque and Florentine styles modernized through her exposure to the *Werkbund* movement at the Munich Academy. "Had Berta Hummel studied in Berlin," Hufnagel continued, "she would have had an entirely different experience."

Berta attended the *Berufsfachschule,* a special section of the Academy that offered a curriculum to prospective teachers of general art in elementary and high schools. Here she had the opportunity to work in a secular environment for the first time, and expand her talents. She studied drawing with Professor Max Dasio, well known for his illustrations in children's books and his woodcuts of German folklore characters. Seizing the opportunity to form, refine, and perhaps influence an emerging talent. Professor Dasio quickly invited Berta Hummel into his inner circle. Eventually, she became Dasio's prize pupil, the student-teacher rapport being so great that he urged her to take a position as his teaching assistant upon her graduation from the Academy.

"Dasio was definitely her most important influence at the Academy," Otto Hufnagel remembered. "Some students arrive at a new school and talk about their past exploits; but Berta Hummel wasn't that way. She made a quick impression on fellow students and professors with her excellent sketching technique. She was quiet, very pretty, and in my opinion a bit withdrawn from the social life that went along with school. Of course, this may have been due to her small-town background and the years she spent away from home in strict religious schools; but at the same time she was clever, possessing a fantastic humor and a quick wit that would pop up when you least expected it. Dasio was a quick-witted person, too, and it was this match of wits that saw them get along so well."

The square, arcaded hallways of the four-story building, skylit by translucent glass roof tiles, were perfect places for Berta Hummel to find quick sketching subjects for Professor Dasio's class. Between classes, students would linger along the balustrades of the arcades, their faces illuminated by pure daylight. Here they kept canvases, smocks, and paints in individual lockers. Often a couple of students would be leaning leisurely against the Corinthian-pillared arcades having a quick conversation, unknowingly becoming the subject of a Berta Hummel sketch. By the time the next class started she would have either presented the sketch to the students or taken it to Professor Dasio for his approval and praise. Today, the battleship gray and white stucco facade of the art school still stands at Richard Wagnerstrasse 10, but the school moved to the Akademiestrasse after the Second World War. The old building now serves as the Paleontological Institute of Munich University.

Sister M. I. Hummel's drawing of "Little Fiddler,"
which is the basis for the HUM 2 figurine.

The old Academy was less than a five-minute walk from the *Alte Pinakothek*, the most famous art museum in Bavaria, where Berta Hummel, along with her fellow students in the color and composition class of Professor Richard Klein, would go to study the works of Albrecht Durer, Rubens, Van Dyck, El Greco, and Murillo. Her visits to this museum brought her close to the masters for the first time. The exposure also served to broaden her scope of art beyond the borders of Germany. "She talked of wanting to go to Florence or Venice to study and paint," her mother remembered.

Berta Hummel's art education was, of course, entirely Bavarian. But the ideas that she picked up during her frequent research visits to the Munich museums, her reading of the art text and biographical commentary on the lives of Giotto, Michelangelo, and the

other masters, combined with the stimulus of the *Werkbund* movement, eventually found their way into her work. Some of it can be seen in the churches in which Sister Innocentia Hummel was commissioned to paint or sculpt a particular religious figure. Her *"Teilbild der Pieta"* ("Mural of Piety") in Tuttlingen, the "Infant of Krumbad" in Krumbad, and the mural at the church of Saint Stephen in Massing of Brother Conrad distributing bread to the poor, are three examples of this art.

Berta Hummel's desire to travel to the great art centers of Europe and her newly focused attention on the old masters came as a shock to both her and her family. The amount of cultural sophistication she had absorbed during her first two years in Munich

completely overshadowed the education and values instilled by her parents and her convent schooling.

She was still, however, very much a product of Catholic Bavaria, of quiet, small-town life that went on with the pace of the horse and buggy or river barge that continued to symbolize transportation in her native area. The attachment to her family was deep, as was the commitment to please her father within the framework of his modest understanding of art. She was familiar with the concepts of sacrifice and self-denial, for they had been articulated since her preschool days, from the *Volksschule* at Massing to the institute in Simbach. These concepts continued to linger quietly but heavily at her side, comprising the weight of the two most important institutions in her life: church and family. Living as a boarding student at the Holy Family residence reminded the happy buzzing bee that after she finished working and gathering knowledge at the Academy, her fate would see her hovering close to home. Thus she was not destined to venture far; the field trips with the watercolor class of Professor Else Brauneis to the Austrian city of Salzburg and the Upper Bavarian resort towns of Garmisch and Partenkirchen were the greatest distances she was to stray.

As in Simbach, the atmosphere of the Holy Family residence was conducted with the strictness of a convent, for it was administered by sisters. Silence was the rule in the hallways, but Berta Hummel always scuffed her heels. Beds were to be made without a wrinkle, but Berta's was always messy. Floors were to be swept clean each morning before breakfast, wardrobes dusted, and sundries kept in order; but Berta Hummel, being the art student in the dormitory, proudly hung her paintings on the walls in violation of the rules, and her pencils, brushes, and paints strewn everywhere across her room. Once again she was the exception to the rules, but once again her talent gained her special friendship and respect. This time it was two young Franciscan Sisters who were staying at the Holy Family residence while studying art at the Akademie. Sister Laura and Sister Kostka were sympathetic toward their new friend and always came to her aid.

Berta's imagination and penchant for doing the things that made her life as a boarding student just a little bit more frivolous managed to overshadow the disciplinary atmosphere of the residence. Instead of rebelling against her superiors, she outwitted them, using her talent and wit to win the sympathy of her sister students when a particular Hummel prank would come to the attention of the Holy Family hierarchy. Male visitors were strictly forbidden, and, as a general rule, relatives and parents were not permitted inside the residence unless approved in advance by the Mother Superior.

One February, Berta Hummel was bemused by the devil-may-care spirit of *Fasching* (Carnival or Mardi Gras) that reigns each year prior to Ash Wednesday. She decided to bend the rules. "She told her Mother Superior that she had invited special visitors to the Holy Family *Fasching* party," Frau Hummel recalled. "But she kept the identity of these visitors a secret for weeks. The Mother Superior thought Berta was going to bring male guests for the celebration."

Compared with what would be going on elsewhere around town, the Holy Family *Fasching* party would be a tame affair. The Bavarian capital took its *Fasching* very seriously, with no holds barred, much like Mardi Gras in New Orleans or Carnival in Rio de Janeiro. The one concession that the superiors made to Berta Hummel was that the affair could be a masked ball—and that gave her all the ammunition she needed. Resident students would be showing up as princes and paupers, soldiers and clowns, and the big worry of the Mother Superior would be how to determine the sex of the guests behind the Hummel-designed masks and costumes. Berta had told the Mother Superior that her guests would be ringing the doorbell around half past eight on carnival night, and once the word got around everyone at the residence was waiting with excitement for the next Hummel coup.

With the sound of the chime, the students all ran down to the parlor to greet the surprise guests with a deeply concerned Mother Superior not far behind. But to their surprise, Berta Hummel had pulled yet another trick out of her seemingly bottomless bag. Standing in the parlor of the Holy Family residence hall were fully clothed papier-mâché models of all her professors: Dasio, Klein, and Brauneis. The Mother Superior was greatly relieved, to say the least.

But playing the role of court jester in a stringent, religious dormitory environment was only one of the sides of Berta Hummel. During this time, her friendship with the two Franciscan Sisters, Sister Laura and Sister Kostka, strengthened, and with it an interest in religious life that hinted her future direction to those around her. "The closer she came to the two sisters," Otto Hufnagel recalled, "the more it became certain that Berta Hummel would eventually join their convent. This irked Dasio very much because she was his prodigy. He wanted her to continue on as his assistant after taking her degree."

Her second year in Munich saw her friendship with the two Franciscan Sisters continue. Her father had just begun to enjoy the happy life he had led before the war. "It had taken him ten years to recover from the war, the hard times, and his shrapnel wounds," said Centa Hummel. "Now, with Vicki's death he became more distant again, and this affected Berta, who was of course a very gentle and emotional person. She was strong in spirit, but she was the kind of person who had so much energy that she would run herself down until her whole body would weaken and she would need to spend weeks on end in bed fighting off the flu. Her reaction to the tragedy was to work harder because she wanted to please her father and become a success. The increased interest in religious life seemed to be her way of giving thanks for all she had. It seemed to represent one part of her personality, and if it was the dominating one she kept it to herself."

The year 1929 gave twenty-year-old Berta Hummel good reason for leaning toward a religious life. Munich, capital of Bavaria and the largest city in southern Germany, had become a haven for the dissatisfied and unemployed; and the magnet that had drawn them was Adolf Hitler's National Socialist German Workers' Party. The marching and singing of the Brownshirts was a common sight during the daytime, and at night the beer halls would fill with the Nazi sympathizers who came to hear Party speakers, drink strong beer, and talk of *Putsch*. At the Academy, students sympathetic to Hitler's cause formed propagandistic youth groups to propagate their ideas and gain new followers among the students of the applied arts.

Upon graduation, the Party would find them jobs, funneling them into critical areas of German culture: advertising, architecture, and graphic design. Waiting in the wings, they would continue their Party activity, organizing for the inevitable political victory that would earn them good positions with the propaganda ministry of Josef Goebbels. Berta Hummel was hardly the kind of individual who wished to tie her educational experience to the success of the Third Reich.

Berta Hummel's bond of friendship with the two Franciscan Sisters brought about changes in her life. "The sisters were regarded as outsiders by most of the students," Otto

A self portrait done by Sister Maria Innocentia Hummel.

Hufnagel said. "They were very quiet and didn't communicate with anyone except their professors and Berta. They would go to class, eat lunch, and disappear." More and more Berta Hummel followed their example.

Berta would pray each morning at the *Frauenkirche* (The Church of Our Lady) before arriving at school. The church, whose twin onion-shaped domes break the skyline across the flat plain of Munich, was on her daily route from Holy Family residence hall to the Academy making it very convenient. The *Frauenkirche* is a majestic structure, ranking as one of the world's outstanding examples of pure Gothic style. Twenty-two octagonal pillars vault the sanctuary roof to a height of one hundred feet, giving a visitor the illusion that all the windows in the church are blocked by its buttresses. Bavarian legend has it that when the devil inspected the church and found no windows, he stamped his foot in delight. In correspondence with this legend, there is a special footprint of the "devil's step" in the vestibule that leads to the cathedral.

Berta Hummel received self-confidence from her religion, for it was the most consistent and dominating theme that ran through her life. The huge *Frauenkirche* in Munich was as much a world away from the small parish church of Saint Stephen in Massing, as the tiny two-level *Volksschule* was from the prestigious Academy. At the age of twenty-two, in 1931, she had come a long way—further than the opportunities of a small-town Bavarian girl would generally suggest. Her artwork at the Academy had given her considerable notoriety among her fellow students, and she held the highest grade point average in her class. As a result, the pressure upon her to make a solid decision about her future was mounting.

On one hand, Professors Max Dasio and Else Brauneis were trying to convince her to continue on at the Academy, both offering to employ her as a graduate teaching assistant. It would have meant a successful, comfortable existence: a secure job, an income, and a leisurely artist's life that revolved around Schwabing, Munich's art colony.

But would this lifestyle remain such a relaxed and fun-filled existence within the changing political climate? There was already a movement on to oust Academy director Carlo Sattler, one of the most important figures in the *Werkbund,* from his position because he was married to a woman with Jewish parentage. Adjusting to this new order would mean a forced break with her entire religious upbringing and education, and a yielding to the chaos and uncertainty of the moment. On the other hand, there was the quiet but persevering example of the two Franciscan Sisters, Laura and Kostka. Seeking sanctuary behind the walls of a convent would permit Berta Hummel to continue her art, to teach, and to live a life that knew a duty only to eternal time instead of the Party, the Reich, or the Führer.

On March 15, 1931, Berta Hummel graduated from the *Akademie fur Angewandte Kunst* in Munich, first in her class. It was a proud day for the entire Hummel family—all of whom went to Munich for the occasion—and especially for her father Adolf, who was seeing his daughter succeed in a métier that to him had been but a fleeting dream. What few knew on that graduation day was that Berta Hummel had already decided upon her destiny. It was a decision made with silence and delicacy, an act that would chafe the feelings of those who held the notion that she would make a much greater contribution to her chosen field in the secular life.

"My parents were not surprised at Berta's decision," Centa Hummel recalled, "for Sisters Laura and Kostka had been to our home in Massing. They knew that Berta was very close to the two Franciscan Sisters and that she was at an important crossroad in her life. But she did keep the actual decision a secret for a period of time. We didn't find out until shortly after her graduation."

Though her parents were not outwardly surprised, Herr Hummel was concerned with his daughter's ability to meet the strenuous demands of religious life. He recalled the disciplinary problems she had incurred at the Massing *Volksschule,* at Simbach, and even at Holy Family. Would Berta Hummel be able to live up to the duties and rules of a convent, he asked his wife. His daughter's decision was the end product of the homelife which he and his wife had supervised, combined with the parochial boarding school education that Herr Hummel himself wished Berta to receive. Berta's Munich years fulfilled her desire to taste the world of art within the secure framework of her religious upbringing. The talent which she refined during her stay there would soon make her name known around the world.

At the Academy in Munich there were sad parting smiles. Berta had made a visit to the home of Professor Else Brauneis to inform her of the decision shortly after graduation. Professor Brauneis was not taken aback by Berta's decision and commenced a lengthy correspondence with her after she entered the convent. But Professor Max Dasio was less enamored with Berta's choice. "She was his cherished pupil," Otto Hufnagel said, "and it was only natural that he felt a degree of disappointment upon finding out. Wouldn't any professor, especially one who was her mentor?" As a going away present, Berta Hummel gave Max Dasio the woodcut of a caricature she had drawn of him. Upon receipt of the gift he looked it over, commenting: "That little rogue of a Hummel could have pulled the drawer out a bit farther." His reference to the "drawer" being his lower lip, which was known to protrude during moments of anger or frustration.

"Dasio finally resigned himself to the fact that Berta had chosen the convent," Centa Hummel said. "He was basically a man who had the philosophy 'everyone does what they will.' " Berta Hummel did exactly that. During the month and a half that passed between her graduation and her prearranged entrance date at the Franciscan Convent at Siessen, she bought new clothing, visited family and acquaintances, and lived a life that hardly reflected her decision to sacrifice all the worldly things she knew and enjoyed. At home in Massing, she spent days quietly sketching, reminiscing, and puttering around the rock garden she had planted when she was younger. But, as Frau Hummel recalled, there was a great deal of emotion upon seeing her off for the journey to Siessen. "We knew she would be coming back to visit," Frau Hummel said, "but we were all concerned with how life at the convent would change her. To us, she would always be Berta."

On April 22, 1931, Berta Hummel entered the convent. The surrounding foothills of the Swabian Alps, greening with spring, were already a familiar sight to her, for she had visited the grounds with Sisters Laura and Kostka a few weeks earlier for a confidential interview. The two sisters had been, of course, an obvious influence on Berta in making her decision to join the Franciscans rather than another Catholic order. Unlike other orders, the Franciscans regard all sisters as equals. There are no choir sisters or lay sisters, no distinctions made between those who have college educations and those who do not. This concept was in keeping with Berta Hummel's humble way of life.

The history of the religious community of Siessen can be traced to the time of the Middle Ages. The name itself, Siessen, means meadowland or pasture, and it was on this kind of terrain outside the town of Saulgau in the old kingdom of Württemberg that in the 13th century a Dominican settlement was formed. During the next six centuries, because of various holy wars, the convent was forced to disband on several occasions. In 1860, while Germany was passing some troublesome years toward a confederation of her many states, the Franciscan Order established a convent around the old nucleus of buildings, creating a teachers' seminary. Later, in 1924, they began devoting themselves to the care of the sick. Their embroidery and lacework also gained them wide renown.

Berta Hummel began teaching art at the teachers' school while a postulant. She also worked with children, traveling by train to several of the sixty-five institutions administered by the Siessen Convent. For a postulant, her schedule was demanding, but she met it. No longer was she the discipline problem that trademarked her previous encounters with religious education. She was taking her work very seriously and her religion as well. On August 22, 1933, she was given her habit of the Sisters of The Third Order of Saint Francis. As the presiding Bishop cut the symbolic lock of hair from her head, he bestowed upon her a new name: Sister Maria Innocentia.

For someone who had so often been preoccupied with the innocence and simplicity of childhood, the name was appropriate. Innocence had clearly been the main theme running through her life, and when admiring the faces of each "M.I. Hummel" figurine the feeling is always present. "The figurines offer the collector something to look back upon," Otto Hufnagel said. "Childhood is one main feeling that radiates. Innocence is another. The romance of youthful nostalgia is everywhere about them, for that was Berta Hummel's style."

CHAPTER
3: SISTER MARIA INNOCENTIA

The lush meadows of the Swabian Highland, carved and scalloped by the Alpine glaciers long ago, gave Sister Maria Innocentia Hummel a classic landscape view from her studio high atop the Motherhouse of the Siessen Convent. Today, Sister Maria Innocentia's studio stands as a small museum, filled with the sketches, tapestries, and vestments that were part of her contribution to religious and secular art as a member of the Franciscan Order.

Out the windows, a patchwork of lush green grazing land and golden windblown wheat fields offered her a timeless picture of nature, a picture that had been in the back of her mind since the early days of her Lower Bavarian childhoold. Between 1931 and 1933 in this bright, sunlit atelier, the Franciscan postulant Berta Hummel worked on her projects.

Her first project, as a visiting art teacher to the school administered at Saulgau, was a strenuous one, and no doubt Berta Hummel was always glad to return to the Motherhouse to work in her studio. She also taught art at the Convent-run school on the Siessen grounds. The local children took a quick liking to the ebullient young postulant,

and some of them would take their Sunday afternoon strolls out to Siessen to visit her. Their reward for the two-mile walk would sometimes be a Hummel sketch. As adults, many of Sister Maria Innocentia's former pupils still make that same walk today.

Another major undertaking of Berta Hummel during her time as a Franciscan postulant was the design of religious vestments and banners, an area in which the Siessen Convent had earned a wide reputation. Applying her talents to further the Convent's long-standing tradition in this field, Berta Hummel saw her concepts in this area reach as far as Africa and Brazil. Some of her designs bore angelic motifs, others included the faces of various saints including Saint Francis, the patron of the Franciscan Order. The vestments and banners, some of them embroidered in fine Japanese gold thread, required an average of 1,000 hours to complete. Still, the quick sketching technique that Berta Hummel mastered at the Munich Academy continued to win the hearts of the young children in her art classes. This, combined with the painstaking work on the religious motifs of the banners and vestments, served to fuse her talents and direct them toward a new phase of artistic development.

"When Sister Innocentia first arrived at the Convent she was searching for artistic direction," Sister Cantalicia, one of the Franciscan Sisters who knew Sister Innocentia at Siessen, said. "She had not yet found her real style, but continued sketching and designing of vestments helped."

According to Sister Berta, another of the Franciscan Sisters who knew Sister Innocentia, the initial impetus to create the sketches which would later become "M.I. Hummel" figurines developed as the result of Berta Hummel's work on her projects. "She had so much energy and a wonderful sense of humor," Sister Berta said.

Berta Hummel's quick wit and marvelous sense of humor did not dull a bit from its sharpness of her Munich Academy days, largely because she used these traits in establishing the teacher-pupil rapport essential for the teaching of kindergarten and grade school. After being given her habit as a member of the Third Order of Saint Francis, Sister Maria Innocentia Hummel created a series of drawings, designed to amuse and reward the young children she was teaching. In November 1933, she took these drawings to a symposium of both lay and religious kindergarten teachers which was being held in the town of Rottenberg am Neckar.

"The drawings were very well received by the symposium," Sister Cantalicia recalled, "and this acceptance gave Sister Innocentia an important feeling of confidence in her work."

As result of this modest acclaim, the name of Sister Maria Innocentia Hummel became so known that several art publishers were vying to distribute her work. Soon, Sister Maria Innocentia Hummel's work was appearing throughout Germany in the form of postcards, not to mention her collaboration with authoress Margareta Seeman on a children's book entitled, *The Hummel Book*. All of Sister Innocentia's artwork created at the convent still is administered by the Siessen Convent, which grants licenses and charges royalty fees for the right to publish Sister Innocentia's work in forms which it sees befitting.

Sister Maria Innocentia Hummel illuminated happiness for her fellow Sisters to reflect upon, too. Her period as a postulant had taught her not only to express herself through the spirit of Saint Francis, but to provide joy to those immediately around her as well. One of the sisters of the Siessen Convent, who first met Sister Innocentia in 1933, recalled an incident in which a fellow sister was particularly sad: "When Sister Innocentia saw the sister's sadness, she glanced at her for a moment and then quietly scurried off to her studio. Later in the day she came to the saddened sister with the sketch of a little duck, bearing the caption *'Kopf hoch und schlucken,'* ('keep your head high and

swallow'). Soon the unhappy sister was in a much better mood." Later, the same sketch would appear in *The Hummel Book*, first published by Emil Finck Verlag in 1934. "Sister Innocentia's wonderful humor and willingness to help others brightened the atmosphere of our Convent," Mother Superior added. "The feeling of innocence and veneration that are present in her artwork are true Franciscan traits."

The bright-eyed smiles of the children in Sister Innocentia's sketches and the guiltless faces of her little angels and Madonnas were unsoiled by the Aryan themes that were being pushed by the propaganda machine of Herr Dr. Goebbels. For many Germans, 1933 was a year of hard times. Adolf Hitler had won power from the caretaker government of an aging von Hindenburg. The theories of Nazism were no longer hot air rising above the crowds in the smoke-clouded beer halls of Munich; they were an overwhelming reality. The work of a humble Franciscan Sister would soon be tantamount to a David, offering a joyous spirit to the soul of a nation, which, in fear of communism, deferred to national socialism and the mustering call of its goliath Third Reich.

But the appeal of the new order was slow in rallying the German artisans. Speedy programs of economic recovery from unemployment and inflation favored the heavy industries, holding large sectors of Bavaria and Thuringia, whose economies depended in large part on the production of porcelain and figurines, in relative disregard.

One of the firms experiencing a slow recovery was the W. Goebel *Porzellanfabrik* in Oeslau, a small town some five miles east of the city of Coburg. The Goebel firm history stemmed from a license to manufacture porcelain and related products granted by the Dukes of Saxe-Coburg-Gotha in 1871. A family-owned company in its fourth generation of proud tradition, the W. Goebel firm employed 350 workers when Franz Goebel first saw the sketches of Sister Maria Innocentia Hummel in 1934.

With a bleak economic outlook, Oeslau, like the other porcelain towns of Germany, was worried. Layoffs at the Goebel factory were imminent, and for Franz Goebel, it would have been a sad day in both the town and company histories if he had had to send those who had devoted lifetimes to the firm into the ranks of the unemployed. Like his father and grandfather, Franz Goebel knew the American market's tastes in porcelain and figurines, and he had lived for short periods in Canada and the United States prior to assuming leadership of the family business. The concept of making the sketches of Sister Maria Innocentia Hummel into ceramic figurines for the export market rang true as one which could bring a much needed economic upswing to his company and the town as well.

Late in 1934 Franz Goebel journeyed to Siessen to share his figurine idea with the Convent in the hope that they would grant him permission to manufacture ceramic figurines from Sister Innocentia's art. At first Sister Innocentia expressed reluctance, but in ensuing discussions both Sister Maria Innocentia Hummel and the Siessen Convent agreed to permit the W. Goebel firm to manufacture ceramic figurines from her two-dimensional artworks, the Convent holding final approval of all figurine designs before they reached the marketplace, just as it does today.

During the winter of 1934-35, Sister Maria Innocentia Hummel made her first trip to the town of Oeslau to advise the W. Goebel craftsmen in the manufacture of figurines based on her artworks. She paid particular attention to color, delicately correcting the blending of special ceramic paints to conform with the colors of her drawings. On other occasions during this development period, artists of the Goebel firm and Franz Goebel himself journeyed to Siessen to hold conferences and present final models for approval. In March 1935, the first "M.I. Hummel" figurines were put on display for export at the Leipzig Trade Fair. The trademark and name "M.I. Hummel," protected internationally, reflects the fact that the figurines are made from the artwork of Sister Maria Innocentia Hummel created during her life as a religious after entering the Siessen Convent on April 22, 1931, and manufactured as three-dimensional ceramic figurines by the W. Goebel firm under an exclusive licensing agreement with the Siessen Convent.

The first "M.I. Hummel" figurines arrived in America in May 1935, and were accepted by the American collectors' market with enough success to warrant W. Goebel's considering the manufacture of new designs based on Sister Innocentia's sketches. These original seven "M.I. Hummel" figurines, models HUM 1 through HUM 10, include some of the most popular and sought-after models on the collecting scene today. Later in that year, the Goebel firm released several more figurines, so that by the end of 1935, HUM 1 through HUM 46 were on the market.

Those who had expressed disappointment over the departure of Berta Hummel from the Munich Academy of Applied Arts in 1931 were happy to see Sister Maria Innocentia Hummel return to the Academy in the fall of 1935. She began a graduate curriculum that centered on painting, and, as a result, spent a great deal of time around the famous museums of Munich, including the *Alte Pinakothek*, studying the masters of the 17th and 18th centuries. She worked in color, chalk, watercolor, charcoal, and oil, experimenting with color and composition. But most of all, Sister Maria Innocentia Hummel continued to perfect her own personal style, best reflected in the "M.I. Hummel" figurines.

During 1936, the demand on the export market was so great that Franz Goebel asked the Siessen Convent for permission to make several new figurines from the artwork of Sister Innocentia. "M.I. Hummel" figurines were a surprising success in America, and one of the biggest outlets for them at the time was the Marshall Field Company of Chicago, the largest department store in the Midwest. Both the Siessen Convent and Sister Innocentia were in accord, and once again a lively exchange took place between Oeslau and Siessen. When the year drew to a close there were another 15 new "M.I. Hummel" figurines, HUM 47 through HUM 62, on the market.

Sister Maria Innocentia Hummel continued to make visits to W. Goebel in Oeslau to inspect the models of her designs and oversee the various production steps in the figurine manufacture to ensure conformity with her artwork. Occasionally Sister Innocentia would suggest a minor change, the brightening of a color, or the positioning of a hat or an umbrella that would conform the figurine to her original artwork and make it more attractive to the collector's eye. The precedents of strict quality control and design review came about due to the excellent working relationship between Franz Goebel and Sister Maria Innocentia Hummel. They are precedents which continue at the Goebel firm today, precedents that have been responsible for the initiation of occasional minor changes in the figurines, often referred to by collectors as "model variations." These will be discussed later in a special chapter.

Unfortunately, Sister Innocentia's second sojourn to Munich was short-lived. She was very busy studying, painting, and drawing during 1936, making trips to Oeslau to supervise the manufacture of "M.I. Hummel" figurines as well. During the fall, she contracted a bad case of the flu and had to withdraw from her advanced studies at the Munich Academy in order to rest and recuperate at the Siessen Motherhouse.

"Sister Innocentia was about five feet six," Sister Cantalicia remembered, "but very thin. She was very energetic, always darting through the halls of the Convent." The ever-present energy was her trademark, typified by the busy little bees she often drew buzzing around her sketches. But in spite of her energy and fervent devotion to God, Sister Innocentia had to make an adjustment in her life.

INNOCENTIA HUMMEL ✝
(1909-1946)

Few woman artists of our day are likely to carry their art to the people in the manner that Sister Innocentia Hummel (Order of Saint Francis) has. Millions of her colorful greeting cards take joy from house to house, and prints of her paintings hang proudly in many homes and businesses. Sister Innocentia has cleverly designed innumerable variations on the theme of joyful, playing children, fresh and roguish as if they had strayed from their mother's watchful eye. The gift of her art was this priceless endowment of joy, radiating a spirit with which everyone can identify.

The call to Heaven will not take Innocentia Hummel's art. For it will always rest on the horizon. It is a testament to her deep feelings, rising with passion to send her message to the people. Her popularity increased even further after her children's sketches were sculpted into ceramic figurines. And in keeping with her Lower Bavarian traditions, Sister Innocentia Hummel took this success in a most quiet and soft-spoken manner.

In the foreground of her life, this youthful Franciscan Sister always stood ready and willing to help others. Those who knew her often had outward apprehensions about her long hours and frail body, but she commanded her talents courageously and each artistic work streamed from her like a song. She once said: "Man must have a light heart (or, translated in another manner, man must be light-hearted) to live beyond his difficulties."

Her life was not without tests. Religious life demanded many sacrifices from her. Her sunny humor was not inherited from her family tradition, but from sacrifice and devotion to God. Innocentia Hummel had a heart which never felt the necessity to say no.

Sister Innocentia Hummel came, as did Brother Konrad von Parzahm, from the valley of the River Rott in Lower Bavaria. An ancestor was the priest and artist Dominikus Hummel (1769-1800). Her father, a merchant. Of six brothers and sisters, she was the third eldest. Beginning in 1921, she attended the Institute of English Sisters in Simbach. In 1927, she began her studies at the Academy for Applied Arts in Munich. She lived with the Sisters of the Holy Family in Blumenstrasse 10. While attending her art classes, she met two Franciscan Sisters from the convent Siessen-Saulgau. After passing her state examination in 1931, she went into seclusion. On August 30, 1934, she was formally inducted into the Franciscan Order.

Shortly thereafter, two books featuring her artwork appeared: *Das Hummel-buch*, by Margareta Seeman (Emil Fink Verlag, Stuttgart, 1934); and a collection of short story illustrations, *Hui, die Hummel*, (Ars-Sacra/Josef Muller Verlag, Munchen). These works reflect the stroke of confidence she had accrued in her descriptions of the children's world.

During her last ten years, the scope of her art broadened. She was commissioned to design altars and murals. The altar painting of Brother Konrad in Saint Stephen's Church in Massing shows her own personal concentration and revelation in the personification of God. One is seized by the deep intimacy that beams from her "Mural of Piety" in Tuttlingen. This work saw her beat a new path, and a style one would hardly expect from an artist such as Sister Innocentia. Her desire for a massive undertaking was rewarded when she was commissioned to design the interior of the cathedral in the Bavarian town of Rathmannsdorf. Sister Innocentia was given the opportunity to spread the tradition of German Catholic art into Africa, but she spurned the offer of the Marienhilfe missionary society, remaining true to her own visions.

It is regrettable that many critics place religious art outside the world of art and culture. Sister Innocentia's exhibitions in the summer of 1946 in Saulgau, and in Friedrichshafen show the many facets and directions of her efforts and prove that the main of the critics have taken a false approach. Her clarity in graphic design brought us religious vestments and wall tapestries, too. Through her expert art pedagogy, she passed her talents on to her co-workers, Sister Laura Brugger and Sister Kostka. On November 6, 1946, the Siessen Convent lost their beloved sister at the very moment the chapel bells tolled noon.

Hugo Schnell

Notes: This obituary is publicly obtainable—extractable from the reference library, fourth floor, Academy of Fine Arts, Akademiestrasse 2, Munchen 40. The bound volume is not removable.

It appeared in the Catholic magazine for art and art history, *Das Munster*, issue spring-fall 1948, published by Verlag Schnell & Steiner, Munich (first year of publication after World War II).

CHAPTER
4: THE FINAL YEARS

Sister Maria Innocentia Hummel.

From 1937 to 1939, Sister Maria Innocentia Hummel's resistance seemed to have lowered. She always had a cold or a flu, and as a result she spent most of her time at work in her studio. At harvest time, when the rest of the Convent would take to the fields, Sister Innocentia was told that she could best serve her fellow sisters from her atelier, letting her spirit partake through her art. By September 1939, Sister Innocentia's strength had not improved. Still, she persevered and garnered the spirit to continue with her artistic pursuits in spite of the Nazi-imposed hardships that so disturbed Convent life. She created countless sketches, some of which were made into "M.I. Hummel" figurines, earning the royalties from the W. Goebel firm that enabled the Siessen Convent to exist in spite of governmental repression. Sister Maria Innocentia Hummel had not yet felt the real mood of the war, nor did she realize that it would put her body and soul to their utmost test.

On February 6, 1937, the Nazi government issued a decree that all Catholic administered schools and other private schools would be systematically closed. At the same time, Berlin raised the taxes of all convents to create a severe economic burden, hoping that institutions like Siessen, with long and proud educational traditions, would eventually collapse. Sister Maria Innocentia Hummel continued her artwork at Siessen during this period. The manufacture of "M.I. Hummel" figurines and the subsequent royalties paid Siessen by the Goebel firm helped the Convent to overcome those hardships.

It was 1940, era of the Battle of Britain. The Berlin government issued a decree that all religious activities in Germany be stopped. On October 31, 1940, Kreisleiter Siller, the local Nazi district leader of Saulgau, and Kreisleiter Drautz of Heilbronn, accompanied by officers of the feared SS, brought SS orders that from that day forth the Siessen Motherhouse would be transformed into an ethnic repatriation center for Germans who had formerly lived in Russia, Romania, Yugoslavia, and Slovenia. Everyone was ordered to leave with their belongings in eight days.

"Send the sisters home," the leaders and administrators of the Convent were told, as the Convent's history book remembers.

Relatives of the Siessen Sisters came from far and wide in automobiles or on trains to help take the Convent's belongings away. Sister Innocentia, like the rest of the Siessen Sisters, reluctantly left the Convent and joined her family in Massing.

"We knew of the hardships," ninety-year-old Viktoria Hummel said, "but we didn't think that Berta would be coming home. She was welcome and we were glad to see her, but all she talked about was going back to the Convent."

Brother Adolf and sister Centa were also very happy to see their sister, but even then her health was in obvious decline. Three weeks after being expelled by the Nazis, Sister Maria Innocentia Hummel received permission to return to the Convent. A few sisters were needed to care for the sick and to perform administrative tasks. "She went back," Centa said of her sister, "because the Convent was her home and her life."

On December 8, 1940, the first 400 repatriated Germans came to Siessen Convent. Eventually that number would jump to 2,000. Sister Innocentia, forced to give up her studio, lived in a damp basement room that also served as her work area.

On January 13, 1941, sensing Catholic sympathies among the refugees, Kreisleiter Drautz of Heilbronn used his power to expropriate all of the Siessen-owned farmland in the name of the Third Reich, to conform with the government food program. All crop harvesting and animal slaughtering, therefore, came under the aegis of the military police, and on July 10, 1941, the local Nazi leaders accused the remaining few Franciscan Sisters of con-

Sister Maria Innocentia Hummel's sketch of madonna and child that became the basis for HUM 48 Madonna Plaque.

The close relationship between Franz Goebel, Sister Maria Innocentia Hummel and the Siessen Convent is emphasized by this 1936 photo taken at the Goebel factory gardens. At left is the Mother Superior of the Siessen Convent, Franz Goebel is in the center and Sister M.I. Hummel at the right.

spiring to use more food than the war plan allowed. Wary of the Franciscan tradition of helping the poor, the Nazis tightened their control over all food produced at Siessen. As a result, the remaining sisters and the refugees lived in virtual famine while the Nazis reaped the bounty of the crops.

The grave food shortages did little to bolster the resistance of Sister Maria Innocentia Hummel, who, in spite of the cramped conditions, continued to sketch with the hope that others would obtain a feeling of veneration from her art. New restrictions were put on firewood and coal, and Sister Innocentia, working in her damp little room, developed complications to a cold which were first diagnosed as pleurisy, later as a lung infection. There were no antibiotics available due to the war effort, nor were there any specialists to look after Sister Innocentia's problem. She underwent a series of chest X-rays in 1940 which tested out negative, but she was still required to spend several weeks recuperating at the Motherhouse.

By the spring of 1941, Sister Maria Innocentia Hummel was once again spending her Sunday afternoons out-of-doors, sketching local children and bringing a priceless quality of joy into the lives of the sisters and the refugees who lived under the siege of Nazism.

In the fall of 1944, Sister Innocentia suffered a relapse of her lung infection, and after she was sent to Wilhelmstift, a hospital at Isny in the Swabian Alps, it was found that her earlier X-rays had been incorrectly read and that, in fact, her condition should have been diagnosed as chronic tuberculosis. She was given the opportunity to travel to neutral Switzerland where she would have received superlative medical attention and had a much better chance for speedy recovery. But she refused to travel alone, and additional travel documents were unavailable. Knowing the finality of her prognosis, Sister Maria Innocentia asked and was allowed to remain at the hospital.

Sister Innocentia tried to live as normal a life as possible, always in good humor and often making sketches to cheer up other patients around her. She decorated the X-ray laboratory so the doctors and technicians would have something more cheerful to look at than wet readings and sore spots. Her reputation known to many at the hospital, Sister Innocentia used only the simple name Maria upon her room door.

On April 11, 1945, the Second World War all but over, Sister Maria Innocentia Hummel departed the hospital sufficiently recovered to return to the Motherhouse. French troops had occupied the area of southwestern Germany surrounding Siessen, and when on April 22, 1945, the town of Saulgau and the Convent were liberated by the French forces, Sister Innocentia returned to Siessen.

By November 1945 she had suffered a relapse. Sister Maria Innocentia Hummel was sent to a Franciscan sanatorium at the town of Wangen, but her condition continued to deteriorate, later becoming complicated by dropsy. Wanting to spend her last days at the Motherhouse, Sister Innocentia was brought to Siessen in September 1946. At noon, on November 6, 1946, the same chapel bells that stood witness to the siege of Nazism tolled out the message that Sister Maria Innocentia Hummel was dead.

CHAPTER
5: THE NAME LIVES ON

When the United States Army occupied the city of Coburg and its surrounding area, production at the W. Goebel firm had already ground to a halt. The firm had contributed to the home front production effort by manufacturing dinnerware of a ceramic nature and a small amount of fine china. Coffee mugs and mess hall plates had been produced for the war effort. But with the collapse of the Third Reich there were not even these orders to be filled. Like all German industry, W. Goebel was on the verge of collapse, but a quirk of political history worked in favor of its fate.

According to the lines drawn up by the four-power treaty at the end of the Second World War, the city of Coburg and the town of Oeslau, location of the Goebel firm, were left in a pocket, surrounded on three sides by communist East Germany and completely cut off from their historic lines of commercial influence. Committed to developing the economy of the border region, the U.S. Military Government quickly lifted the wartime embargo and granted the W. Goebel firm a permit to manufacture and export "M.I. Hummel" figurines and other collectors items. Some of the first postwar collectors were the GIs stationed in Germany with the American occupation forces.

By 1949 the Federal Republic of Germany had been formed, the Marshall Plan was sparking reconstruction, and production at W. Goebel was in full swing. Factory worker strength was at an all time high of 800. The combination of prewar collectors anxious to acquire new figurines, ex-GIs and their families, and civilian employees of the U.S. Government who were spending tours of duty in Germany brought continued collector interest on the home front. At the same time, the constantly rotating army of soldiers of the occupation force discovered the "M.I. Hummel" experience in West Germany and brought the figurines back home.

For the American GIs stationed in West Germany, "M.I. Hummel" figurine collecting was an inexpensive and constructive pastime that broke the droll monotony of restrictive barracks life. GIs on weekend passes and increasing numbers of American tourists would scour German towns for "M.I. Hummel" figurines, building their collections and above all using the common interest in collecting to spread goodwill and better German-American relations.

In this reconstruction era of black-market food and irregular currency speculation, "M.I. Hummel" figurines were often purchasable at what would be considered extreme bargain prices by today's standards. Until the summer of 1958, the U.S. Army in Germany paid its troops in Military Payment Certificates (MPC)—similar to the system used in Viet Nam—in an attempt to keep U.S. dollars off the German black market. GIs could exchange these MPC at military banking facilities at a fixed rate of exchange—approximately 4.75 German marks for every dollar—but they always found a more lucrative exchange with the German taxi drivers, who paid at a rate of six marks to each U.S. MPC dollar. Tourists with real greenbacks found an even higher rate of exchange.

Through shrewd currency bargaining, GIs and tourists could purchase their "M.I. Hummel" figurines at normal retail price, in reality paying only one-half to two-thirds the cost due to the unofficial rates of exchange. In July 1958, the U.S. Army called in all

The W. Goebel factory in 1914.

of its MPC and began paying the troops in greenbacks. Exchange rates stabilized somewhat, but with more greenbacks and collectors floating around Germany, "Hummel fever" continued, giving birth to countless collections of figurines that are very difficult to find today.

Though U.S. servicemen and American tourists in Europe helped broaden "M.I. Hummel" collecting interest, the Hummel experience is shared by the broadest spectrum of American society. With millions of collectors in the United States alone, Hummel collecting has become one of America's national pastimes. The U.S. government recognized this in 1952 when the Treasury Department designated "M.I. Hummel" figurines as works of art.

CHAPTER 6: THE COLLECTION

Here is the revised and fully-authorized documentation of the complete collection of "M.I. Hummel" figurines, plates, plaques and all other art objects. This is the most definitive listing and photographic collection ever assembled.

This list, compiled from the W. Goebel production journal in Rödental, West Germany, constitutes a record of all "M.I. Hummel" figurines that have been authorized for production. "M.I. Hummel" figurine identification numbers run in ascending order from 1 to 701. English and German names of the figurines as well as their sizes and notes on most models will be found in the special annotated listing.

All sizes are approximate and depend upon exact method of measurement. Minor variations occur frequently and therefore should not be considered significant.

"M.I. Hummel" figurine identification numbers and their corresponding figurines are divided into five distinct categories:

Open Edition (OE): Pieces currently in W. Goebel's production program.

Closed Edition (CE): Pieces formerly in W. Goebel's production program but no longer produced.

Open Number (ON): An identification number, which in W. Goebel's numerical identification system has not yet been used, but which may be used to identify new "M.I. Hummel" figurines as they are released in the future.

Closed Number (CN): An identification number in W. Goebel's numerical identification system that was used to identify a design or sample models for possible production, but then for various reasons never authorized for release.

Possible Future Edition (PFE): Pieces that have been designed and approved for production and possible release in future years.

INCISED HUM No.	NAME	SIZES	STATUS
1	**Puppy Love**/*Geigerlein mit Hund*	5 to 5¼"	OE
2/0	**Little Fiddler**/*Geigerlein ohne Hund*	5¾ to 6½"	OE
2/I	**Little Fiddler**/*Geigerlein ohne Hund*	7½"	OE
2/II	**Little Fiddler**/*Geigerlein ohne Hund*	10¾"	OE
2/III (2/3)	**Little Fiddler**/*Geigerlein ohne Hund*	12¼"	OE
3/I	**Book Worm**/*Der Bücherwurm*	5½"	OE
3/II (3/2)	**Book Worm**/*Der Bücherwurm*	8"	OE
3/III (3/3)	**Book Worm**/*Der Bücherwurm*	9 to 9½"	OE
4	**Little Fiddler**/*Geigerlein ohne Hund*	4¾ to 5¾"	OE
5	**Strolling Along**/*Wanderbub mit Hund*	4¾ to 5¼"	OE
6.	**Sensitive Hunter**/*Jägerlein*	5"	CE
6/0	**Sensitive Hunter**/*Jägerlein*	4¾"	OE
6/I	**Sensitive Hunter**/*Jägerlein*	5½"	OE
6/II	**Sensitive Hunter**/*Jägerlein*	7 to 7½"	OE
7/0	**Merry Wanderer**/*Wanderbub ohne Hund*	6 to 6¼"	OE
7/I	**Merry Wanderer**/*Wanderbub ohne Hund*	7 to 8"	OE
7/II (7/2)	**Merry Wanderer**/*Wanderbub ohne Hund*	9½ to 10"	OE
7/III	**Merry Wanderer**/*Wanderbub ohne Hund*	11 to 12"	OE
7/X	**Merry Wanderer**/*Wanderbub ohne Hund*	32"	OE
8	**Book Worm**/*Der Bücherwurm*	4 to 4½"	OE
9	**Begging His Share**/*Gratulant*	5¼ to 6"	OE
10/I	**Flower Madonna (Open Halo)**/*Blumen-Madonna mit Kind (offener Heiligenschein)*	9 to 9½"	CE
10/I	**Flower Madonna (Closed Halo)**/*Blumen-Madonna mit Kind (geschlossener Heiligenschein)*	7¾ to 8¼"	OE
10.	**Flower Madonna (Open Halo)**/*Blumen-Madonna mit Kind (offener Heiligenschein)*	12"	CE
10/III (10/3)	**Flower Madonna (Open Halo)**/*Blumen-Madonna mit Kind (offener Heiligenschein)*	12 to 13"	CE
10/III	**Flower Madonna (Closed Halo)**/*Blumen-Madonna mit Kind (geschlossener Heiligenschein)*	11 to 11½"	OE

INCISED HUM No.	NAME	SIZES	STATUS
11.	**Merry Wanderer**/*Wanderbub ohne Hund*	4¾"	CE
11 2/0	**Merry Wanderer**/*Wanderbub ohne Hund*	4¼ to 4½"	OE
11/0	**Merry Wanderer**/*Wanderbub ohne Hund*	4¾ to 5"	OE
12 2/0	**Chimney Sweep**/*Ich bringe Glück, Kaminfeger*	4 to 4¼"	OE
12/1	**Chimney Sweep**/*Ich bringe Glück, Kaminfeger*	5½ to 6½"	OE
12.	**Chimney Sweep**/*Ich bringe Glück, Kaminfeger*	6 to 6¼"	CE
13/2/0	**Meditation**/*Die Gratulantin*	4¼"	OE
13/0	**Meditation**/*Die Gratulantin*	5 to 6"	OE
13/II (13/2)	**Meditation**/*Die Gratulantin*	7 to 7¼"	OE
13/V (13/5)	**Meditation**/*Die Gratulantin*	13¼ to 14"	OE
14 A & B	**Book Worm, Book Ends, Boy and Girl**/*Buchstützen, Der Bücherwurm, Junge und Mädchen*	5½"	OE
15/0	**Hear Ye, Hear Ye**/*Hört Ihr Leute, Nachtwächter*	5 to 5¼"	OE
15/I	**Hear Ye, Hear Ye**/*Hört Ihr Leute, Nachtwächter*	6 to 6¼"	OE
15/II (15/2)	**Hear Ye, Hear Ye**/*Hört Ihr Leute, Nachtwächter*	7 to 7½"	OE
16 2/0	**Little Hiker**/*Hans im Glück*	3¾ to 4¼"	OE
16/1	**Little Hiker**/*Hans im Glück*	5½ to 6"	OE
16.	**Little Hiker**/*Hans im Glück*	5½ to 5¾"	CE
17/0	**Congratulations**/*Ich Gratuliere*	5½ to 6"	CE
17	**Congratulations**/*Ich Gratuliere*	6"	OE
17/II (17/2)	**Congratulations**/*Ich Gratuliere*	7¾ to 8¼"	CE
18	**Christ Child**/*Stille Nacht, Jesuskind*	3¼ x 6 to 3¾ x 6½"	OE
19	**Prayer Before Battle on Big Round Tray**/*Der fromme Reitersmann auf grossem runden Tablett*		CN
20	**Prayer Before Battle**/*Der fromme Reitersmann*	4 to 4¼"	OE
21/0	**Heavenly Angel**/*Christkindlein kommt, Engel*	4 to 4¾"	OE
21/0 ½	**Heavenly Angel**/*Christkindlein kommt, Engel*	5¾ to 6½"	OE
21/I	**Heavenly Angel**/*Christkindlein kommt, Engel*	6¾ to 7¼"	OE
21/II	**Heavenly Angel**/*Christkindlein kommt, Engel*	8½ to 8¾"	OE
22.	**Holy Water Font, Sitting Angel**/*Weihkessel, sitzender Engel*	3⅛ x 4½"	CE
22/0	**Holy Water Font, Sitting Angel**/*Weihkessel, sitzender Engel*	3 x 4"	OE
22/I	**Holy Water Font, Sitting Angel**/*Weihkessel, sitzender Engel*	3½ x 4⅞"	OE
23/I	**Adoration**/*Bei Mutter Maria, Marterl*	6¼ to 7"	OE
23/III (23/3)	**Adoration**/*Bei Mutter Maria, Marterl*	8¾ to 9"	OE
24/I	**Lullaby, Candle Holder**/*Wiegenlied mit Kerzentülle*	3½ x 5 to 5½"	OE
24/III (24/3)	**Lullaby, Candle Holder**/*Wiegenlied mit Kerzentülle*	6¼ x 8¾"	OE
25	**Angelic Sleep, Candle Holder**/*Stille Nacht mit Kerzentülle*	3½ x 5 to 5½"	OE
26/0	**Holy Water Font, Child Jesus**/*Weihkessel, Christkindlein*	2¾ x 5¼"	OE
26/I	**Holy Water Font, Child Jesus**/*Weihkessel, Christkindlein*	3¼ x 6"	OE
27/I	**Joyous News, Candle Holder**/*O, du fröhliche mit Kerzentülle*	2¾"	CE
27/III (27/3)	**Joyous News**/*O, du fröhliche*	4¼ x 4¾"	OE
28/II (28/2)	**Wayside Devotion**/*Abendlied, Marterl*	7 to 7½"	OE
28/III	**Wayside Devotion**/*Abendlied, Marterl*	8¾"	OE
29.	**Holy Water Font, Guardian Angel**/*Weihkessel, Schutzengel*	2½ x 5¾"	CE
29/0	**Holy Water Font, Guardian Angel**/*Weihkessel, Schutzengel*	2⅞ x 6"	CE
29/I	**Holy Water Font, Guardian Angel**/*Weihkessel, Schutzengel*	3 x 6⅜"	CE
30 A & B	**Ba-Bee Rings, Boy and Girl**/*Hui, die Hummel, Junge und Mädchen, Wandringe*	4¾ x 5"	OE
30/0 A & B	**Ba-Bee Rings, Boy and Girl**/*Hui, die Hummel, Junge und Mädchen, Wandringe*	4¾ x 5"	CE
30/I A & B	**Ba-Bee Rings, Boy and Girl**/*Hui, die Hummel, Junge und Mädchen, Wandringe*	5¼ x 6	CE
31	**Silent Night with Black Child**/*Stille Nacht, Krippe mit schwarzem Kindlein*	3½ x 5"	CE
32	**Little Gabriel**/*O, du fröhliche..., Engel*	5"	OE
32/0	**Little Gabriel**/*O, du fröhliche..., Engel*	5 to 5½"	CE
32/I	**Little Gabriel**/*O, du fröhliche..., Engel*	5¾ to 6"	CE
33	**Joyful, Ashtray**/*Ascher, Gesangsprobe*	3½ x 6"	OE
34	**Singing Lesson, Ashtray**/*Ascher, 's stimmt net*	3½ x 6¼"	OE
35/0	**Holy Water Font, The Good Shepherd**/*Weihkessel: Der gute Hirte*	2½ x 4¾"	OE
35/I	**Holy Water Font, The Good Shepherd**/*Weihkessel: Der gute Hirte*	2¾ x 5¾"	OE
36/0	**Holy Water Font, Child with Flowers**/*Weihkessel, Kind mit Blumen*	3¼ x 4¼"	OE

INCISED HUM No.	NAME	SIZES	STATUS
36/I	**Holy Water Font, Child with Flowers**/*Weihkessel, Kind mit Blumen*	3½ x 4½″	OE
36.	**Holy Water Font, Child with Flowers**/*Weihkessel, Kind mit Blumen*	3½ x 4½″	CE
37	**Herald Angels, Candle Holder**/*Adventsleuchter mit drei Engeln*	2¾ x 4 to 4½″	OE
1/38/0	**Angel Joyous News, with Lute, Candle Holder**/*Adventsengelchen mit Laute, mit Kerzentülle*	2 to 2¼″	OE
III/38/0	**Angel Joyous News, with Lute, Candle Holder**/*Adventsengelchen mit Laute, mit Kerzentülle*	2 to 2¼″	OE
III/38/I	**Angel Joyous News, with Lute, Candle Holder**/*Adventsengelchen mit Laute, mit Kerzentülle*	2¾″	OE
1/39/0	**Angel Joyous News, with Accordion, Candle Holder**/*Adventsengelchen mit Bandoneon, mit Kerzentülle*	2 to 2¼″	OE
III/39/0	**Angel Joyous News, with Accordion, Candle Holder**/*Adventsengelchen mit Bandoneon, mit Kerzentülle*	2 to 2¼″	OE
III/39/I	**Angel Joyous News, with Accordion, Candle Holder**/*Adventsengelchen mit Bandoneon, mit Kerzentülle*	2¾″	OE
I/40/0	**Angel Joyous News, with Trumpet, Candle Holder**/*Adventsengelchen mit Trompete, mit Kerzentülle*	2 to 2¼″	OE
III/40/0	**Angel Joyous News, with Trumpet, Candle Holder**/*Adventsengelchen mit Trompete, mit Kerzentülle*	2 to 2¼″	OE
III/40/I	**Angel Joyous News, with Trumpet, Candleholder**/*Adventsengelchen mit Trompete, mit Kerzentülle*	2¾″	OE
41	**Singing Lesson (without base)**/*'s stimmt net (ohne Fuss)*		CN
42	**Good Shepherd**/*Der gute Hirte*	6¼″	OE
42/0	**Good Shepherd**/*Der gute Hirte*	6¼ to 6½″	CE
42/I	**Good Shepherd**/*Der gute Hirte*	7¼ to 7¾″	CE
43	**March Winds**/*Lausbub*	4¾ to 5½″	OE
44 A	**Culprits, Table Lamp**/*Apfeldieb, Junge, Lampenfuss*	8½ to 9½″	OE
44 B	**Out of Danger, Table Lamp**/*In Sicherheit, Mädchen, Lampenfuss*	8½ to 9½″	OE
45/0	**Madonna with Halo**/*Madonna mit Heiligenschein*	10½″	OE
45/I	**Madonna with Halo**/*Madonna mit Heiligenschein*	11½ to 13¼″	OE
45/III (45/3)	**Madonna with Halo**/*Madonna mit Heiligenschein*	15½ to 16¾″	OE
46/0	**Madonna without Halo**/*Madonna ohne Heiligenschein*	10¼″	OE
46/I	**Madonna without Halo**/*Madonna ohne Heiligenschein*	11¼ to 13″	OE
46/III (46/3)	**Madonna without Halo**/*Madonna ohne Heiligenschein*	15¼ to 16¼″	OE
47 3/0	**Goose Girl**/*Gänseliesl*	4 to 4¼″	OE
47/0	**Goose Girl**/*Gänseliesl*	4¾ to 5¼″	OE
47/II (47/2)	**Goose Girl**/*Gänseliesl*	7 to 7½″	OE
48/0	**Madonna Plaque**/*Madonnenbild*	3¼ x 4¼″	OE
48/II (48/2)	**Madonna Plaque**/*Madonnenbild*	4¾ x 5¾″	OE
48/V (48/5)	**Madonna Plaque**/*Madonnenbild*	8¾ x 10¾″	CE
49 3/0	**To Market**/*Brüderlein und Schwesterlein*	4″	OE
49/0	**To Market**/*Brüderlein und Schwesterlein*	5 to 5½″	OE
49/I	**To Market**/*Brüderlein und Schwesterlein*	6¼ to 6½″	OE
49.	**To Market**/*Brüderlein und Schwesterlein*	6¼ to 6½″	CE
50 2/0	**Volunteers**/*Soldatenspiel*	4¾ to 5″	OE
50/0	**Volunteers**/*Soldatenspiel*	5½ to 6″	OE
50/I	**Volunteers**/*Soldatenspiel*	6½ to 7″	OE
50.	**Volunteers**/*Soldatenspiel*	7″	CE
51 3/0	**Village Boy**/*Dorfbub*	4″	OE
51 2/0	**Village Boy**/*Dorfbub*	5″	OE
51/0	**Village Boy**/*Dorfbub*	6 to 6¾″	OE
51/1	**Village Boy**/*Dorfbub*	7¼ to 8″	OE
52/0	**Going to Grandma's**/*Hausmütterchen*	4½ to 5″	OE
52/1	**Going to Grandma's**/*Hausmütterchen*	6 to 6¼″	OE
52.	**Going to Grandma's**/*Hausmütterchen*	6¼″	CE
53	**Joyful**/*Gesangsprobe*	3½ to 4¼″	OE
III/53	**Joyful, Box (Bowl Style)**/*Gesangsprobe, Dose (Schüsselform)*	6½″	CE
III/53	**Joyful, Box (Jar Style)**/*Gesangsprobe, Dose (Zylindrische Form)*	5¾″	OE
54	**Silent Night, Candle Holder**/*Stille Nacht, Krippe mit Kerzentülle*	3½ x 4¾″	OE
55	**Saint George**/*Ritter Heiliger Georg*	6¾″	OE
56 A	**Culprits**/*Apfeldieb, Junge*	6¼ to 6¾″	OE
56 B	**Out of Danger**/*In Sicherheit, Mädchen*	6¼ to 6¾″	OE

INCISED HUM No.	NAME	SIZES	STATUS
57/0	**Chick Girl**/*Kükenmütterchen*	3½"	OE
57/I	**Chick Girl**/*Kükenmütterchen*	4¼"	OE
57.	**Chick Girl**/*Kükenmütterchen*	4 to 4⅜"	CE
III/57	**Chick Girl, Box (Bowl Style)**/*Kükenmütterchen, Dose (Schüsselform)*	6 to 6¼"	CE
III/57	**Chick Girl, Box (Jar Style)**/*Kükenmütterchen, Dose (Zylindrische Form)*	5"	OE
58/0	**Playmates**/*Hasenvater*	4"	OE
58/I	**Playmates**/*Hasenvater*	4¼"	OE
III/58	**Playmates, Box (Bowl Style)**/*Hasenvater, Dose (Schüsselform)*	6¾"	CE
III/58	**Playmates, Box (Jar Style)**/*Hasenvater, Dose (Zylindrische Form)*	5½"	OE
59	**Skier**/*Ski-Heil*	5 to 6"	OE
60 A	**Book End, Farm Boy**/*Buchstütze, Schweinehirt*	4¾"	OE
60 B	**Book End, Goose Girl**/*Buchstütze, Gänseliesl*	4¾"	OE
61 A	**Book End, Playmates**/*Buchstütze, Hasenvater*	4"	OE
61 B	**Book End, Chick Girl**/*Buchstütze, Kükenmütterchen*	4"	OE
62	**Happy Pastime, Ashtray**/*Ascher, Strickliesl*	3½ x 6¼"	OE
63	**Singing Lesson**/*'s stimmt net*	2¾ to 3"	OE
III/63	**Singing Lesson, Box (Bowl Style)**/*'s stimmt net, Dose (Schüsselform)*	5¾"	CE
III/63	**Singing Lesson, Box (Jar Style)**/*'s stimmt net, Dose (Zylindrische Form)*	4¾"	OE
64	**Shepherd's Boy**/*Schäferbub*	5½ to 6¼"	OE
65	**Farewell**/*Auf Wiedersehen*	4¾"	OE
65/0	**Farewell**/*Auf Wiedersehen*	4"	CE
65/I	**Farewell**/*Auf Wiedersehen*	4½ to 4⅞"	CE
65.	**Farewell**/*Auf Wiedersehen*	4¾ to 5"	CE
66	**Farm Boy**/*Schweinehirt*	5 to 5¾"	OE
67	**Doll Mother**/*Puppenmütterchen*	4¼ to 4¾"	OE
68 2/0	**Lost Sheep**/*Schäferbub*	4¼ to 4½"	OE
68/0	**Lost Sheep**/*Schäferbub*	5½"	OE
68.	**Lost Sheep**/*Schäferbub*	5½ to 6½"	CE
69	**Happy Pastime**/*Strickliesl*	3½"	OE
III/69	**Happy Pastime, Box (Bowl Style)**/*Strickliesl, Dose (Schüsselform)*	6½"	CE
III/69	**Happy Pastime, Box (Jar Style)**/*Strickliesl, Dose (Zylindrische Form)*	5¼"	OE
70	**The Holy Child**/*Jesulein*	6¾ to 7½"	OE
71	**Stormy Weather**/*Unter einem Dach*	6 to 7"	OE
72	**Spring Cheer**/*Frühling ist's*	5 to 5½"	OE
73	**Little Helper**/*Fleissiges Lieschen*	4¼ to 4½"	OE
74	**Little Gardener**/*Die kleine Gärtnerin*	4 to 4½"	OE
75	**Holy Water Font, White Angel**/*Weihkessel, weisser Engel*	3¼ x 4½"	OE
76 A&B	**Book Ends, Doll Mother & Prayer Before Battle**/*Buchstützen, Puppenmütterchen und Der fromme Reitersmann*		CE
77	**Holy Water Font, Cross with Doves**/*Weihkessel, Kreuz mit Tauben*	1¾ x 6¼"	CN
78/0	**Infant of Krumbad**/*Jesuskind, liegend*	2¼"	CE
78/1	**Infant of Krumbad**/*Jesuskind, liegend*	2½"	OE
78/II	**Infant of Krumbad**/*Jesuskind, liegend*	3½"	OE
78/III (78/3)	**Infant of Krumbad**/*Jesuskind, liegend*	4½ to 5¼"	OE
78/V	**Infant of Krumbad**/*Jesuskind, liegend*	7½ to 7¾"	OE
78/VI (78/6)	**Infant of Krumbad**/*Jesuskind, liegend*	10 to 11¼"	OE
78/VIII	**Infant of Krumbad**/*Jesuskind, liegend*	13¼ to 14¼"	OE
79	**Globe Trotter**/*Hinaus in die Ferne*	5 to 5¼"	OE
80	**Little Scholar**/*Erster Schulgang, Junge*	5¼ to 5¾"	OE
81 2/0	**School Girl**/*Erster Schulgang, Mädchen*	4¼ to 4¾"	OE
81/0	**School Girl**/*Erster Schulgang, Mädchen*	4¾ to 5¼"	OE
81.	**School Girl**/*Erster Schulgang, Mädchen*	5⅛ to 5½"	CE
82 2/0	**School Boy**/*Schulschwänzer, Junge*	4 to 4½"	OE
82/0	**School Boy**/*Schulschwänzer, Junge*	4¾ to 6"	OE
82/II (82/2)	**School Boy**/*Schulschwänzer, Junge*	7½"	OE
83	**Angel Serenade**/*Fromme Weisen*	5½ to 5¾"	OE
84/0	**Worship**/*Am Wegesrand, Bildstöckl*	5 to 5½"	OE
84/V (84/5)	**Worship**/*Am Wegesrand, Bildstöckl*	12½ to 13¼"	OE
84.	**Worship**/*Am Wegesrand, Bildstöckl*	5¼"	CE
85/0	**Serenade**/*Ständchen, Junge mit Flöte*	4¾ to 5¼"	OE
85/II (85/2)	**Serenade**/*Ständchen, Junge mit Flöte*	7 to 7½"	OE
86	**Happiness**/*Wanderlied, Mädchen*	4½ to 5"	OE

INCISED HUM No.	NAME	SIZES	STATUS
87	**For Father**/*Fürs Vaterle, Rettichbub*	5½″	OE
88/I	**Heavenly Protection**/*Schutzengel*	6¼ to 6¾″	OE
88/II	**Heavenly Protection**/*Schutzengel*	8¾ to 9″	OE
88.	**Heavenly Protection**/*Schutzengel*	9¼″	CE
89/I	**Little Cellist**/*Heimkehr, Bassgeiger*	5¼ to 6¼″	OE
89/II (89/2)	**Little Cellist**/*Heimkehr, Bassgeiger*	7½ to 7¾″	OE
90 A & B	**Book Ends, Eventide & Adoration (without shrine)**/*Buchstützen, Abendlied und Bei Mutter Maria (ohne Marterl)*		CE
91 A	**Holy Water Font, Angel facing left**/*Weihkessel, Engel linksschauend*	3⅜ x 5″	OE
91 B	**Holy Water Font, Angel facing right**/*Weihkessel, Engel rechtsschauend*	3⅜ x 5″	OE
91 A	**Holy Water Font, Angel facing left (without halo)**/*Weihkessel, Engel linksschauend (ohne Heiligenschein)*	3¼ x 4½″	CE
91 B	**Holy Water Font, Angel facing right (without halo)**/*Weihkessel, Engel rechtsschauend (ohne Heiligenschein)*	3¼ x 4½″	CE
92	**Merry Wanderer, Wall Plaque**/*Bild, Wanderbub*	4½ x 5 to 5 x 5½″	OE
93	**Little Fiddler, Wall Plaque**/*Bild, Geigerlein*	4½ x 5 to 5 x 5½″	OE
94 3/0	**Surprise**/*Hänsel und Gretel*	4 to 4¼″	OE
94/I	**Surprise**/*Hänsel und Gretel*	5¼ to 5½″	OE
94.	**Surprise**/*Hänsel und Gretel*	5¾″	CE
95	**Brother**/*Dorfheld*	5¼ to 5¾″	OE
96	**Little Shopper**/*Gretel*	4½ to 5″	OE
97	**Trumpet Boy**/*Der kleine Musikant*	4½ to 4¾″	OE
98 2/0	**Sister**/*Der erste Einkauf*	4½ to 4¾″	OE
98/0	**Sister**/*Der erste Einkauf*	5¼ to 5½″	OE
98.	**Sister**/*Der erste Einkauf*	5¾″	CE
99	**Eventide**/*Abendlied*	4¼ x 5″	OE
100	**Shrine, Table Lamp**/*Marterl, Lampenfuss mit Figur*	7½″	CE
101 (II/101)	**To Market, Table Lamp**/*Brüderlein und Schwesterlein, Lampenfuss*	7½″	CE
102	**Volunteers, Table Lamp**/*Soldatenspiel, Lampenfuss*		CE
103	**Farewell, Table Lamp**/*Auf Wiedersehen, Lampenfuss*		CE
104	**Wayside Devotion, Table Lamp**/*Abendlied, Marterl, Lampenfuss*		CE
105	**Adoration with Bird**/*Bei Mutter Maria, Marterl mit Vogel*	4¾″	CE
106	**Merry Wanderer, Wall Plaque with Wood Frame**/*Wanderbub, Bild mit Holzrahmen*	6 x 6″	CE
107	**Little Fiddler, Wall Plaque with Wood Frame**/*Geigerlein, Bild mit Holzrahmen*	6 x 6″	CE
108	**Angel with Two Children at Feet**/*Engel mit zwei Kindern zu Füssen*		CN
109	**Happy Traveller**/*Hinaus in die Ferne*	5″	OE
109/0	**Happy Traveller**/*Hinaus in die Ferne*	4¾ to 5″	OE
109/II	**Happy Traveller**/*Hinaus in die Ferne*	7½″	OE
109.	**Happy Traveller**/*Hinaus in die Ferne*	7¾″	CE
110/0	**Let's Sing**/*Heini, Bandoneonspieler*	3 to 3¼″	OE
110/I	**Let's Sing**/*Heini, Bandoneonspieler*	3½ to 4″	OE
110	**Let's Sing**/*Heini, Bandoneonspieler*	4″	CE
III/110	**Let's Sing, Box (Bowl Style)**/*Heini, Bandoneonspieler, Dose (Schüsselform)*	6¼″	CE
III/110	**Let's Sing, Box (Jar Style)**/*Heini, Bandoneonspieler, Dose (Zylindrische Form)*	5¼″	OE
111 3/0	**Wayside Harmony**/*Vaters G'scheitester*	3¾ to 4″	OE
111/I	**Wayside Harmony**/*Vaters G'scheitester*	5 to 5½″	OE
111.	**Wayside Harmony**/*Vaters G'scheitester*	5½″	CE
II/111	**Wayside Harmony, Table Lamp**/*Vaters G'scheitester, Lampenfuss*	7½″	CE
112 3/0	**Just Resting**/*Mutters Liebste*	3¾ to 4″	OE
112/I	**Just Resting**/*Mutters Liebste*	4¾ to 5½″	OE
112.	**Just Resting**/*Mutters Liebste*	5½″	CE
II/112	**Just Resting, Table Lamp**/*Mutters Liebste, Lampenfuss*	7½″	CE
113	**Heavenly Song, Candle Holder**/*Stille Nacht, Adventsgruppe, Leuchter*	3½ x 4¾″	OE
114	**Let's Sing, Ashtray**/*Heini, Bandoneonspieler, Ascher*	3½ x 6¼″	OE
115	**Advent Candlestick, Girl with nosegay**/*Adventsleuchter, Mädchen mit Blumenstrauss*	3½″	OE
116	**Advent Candlestick, Girl with fir tree**/*Adventsleuchter, Mädchen mit Tannenbaum*	3½″	OE
117	**Advent Candlestick, Boy with horse**/*Adventsleuchter, Junge mit Holzpferd*	3½″	OE

INCISED HUM No.	NAME	SIZES	STATUS
118	**Little Thrifty, Bank**/*Spar-Hummelchen*	5 to 5½″	OE
119	**Postman**/*Eilbote*	5 to 5½″	OE
120	**Book Ends, Joyful and Let's Sing (on wooden base)**/*Buchstützen, Gesangsprobe und Heini, Bandoneonspieler (auf Holzfuss)*		CE
121	**Book Ends, Wayside Harmony and Just Resting (on wooden base)**/*Buchstützen, Vaters G'scheitester und Mutters Liebste (auf Holzfuss)*		CE
122	**Book Ends, Puppy Love and Serenade with Dog (on wooden base)**/*Buchstützen, Geigerlein und Ständchen mit Hund (auf Holzfuss)*		CE
123	**Max and Moritz**/*Max und Moritz*	5 to 5½″	OE
124/0	**Hello**/*Chef*	5¾ to 6¼″	OE
124/I	**Hello**/*Chef*	6¾ to 7″	OE
124.	**Hello**/*Chef*	6½″	CE
125	**Vacation-Time, Plaque (Old Style)**/*Ferienfreude, Bild (alter Stil)*	4⅜ x 5¼″	CE
125	**Vacation-Time, Plaque (New Style)**/*Ferienfreude, Bild (neuer Stil)*	4 x 4¾″	OE
126	**Retreat to Safety, Plaque**/*Bild, Angsthase*	4¾ x 4¾ to 5 x 5″	OE
127	**Doctor**/*Puppendoktor*	4¾ to 5¼″	OE
128	**Baker**/*Der kleine Konditor*	4¾ to 5″	OE
129	**Band Leader**/*Herr Kapellmeister*	5 to 5⅞″	OE
130	**Duet**/*Duett, Sängerpaar*	5 to 5½″	OE
131	**Street Singer**/*Kammersänger*	5 to 5½″	OE
132	**Star Gazer**/*Sterngucker*	4¾″	OE
133	**Mother's Helper**/*Mutters Stütze*	4¾ to 5″	OE
134	**Quartet, Wall Plaque**/*"Das Quartett," Bild*	5½ x 6¼″	OE
135	**Soloist**/*Heldentenor*	4½ to 5″	OE
136/I	**Friends**/*Gute Freunde*	5″	OE
(136/5) 136/V	**Friends**/*Gute Freunde*	10¾ to 11″	OE
136.	**Friends**/*Gute Freunde*	10½″	CE
137 A	**Wall Plaque, Child in Bed, looking left**/*Bild, Kind im Bett, linksschauend*	2¾ x 2¾″	CE
137 B	**Wall Plaque, Child in Bed, looking right**/*Bild, Kind im Bett, rechtsschauend*	2¾ x 2¾″	CE
137	**Wall Plaque, Child in Bed, looking right**/*Bild, Kind im Bett, rechtsschauend*	2¾ x 2¾″	OE
138	**Wall Plaque, Tiny Baby in Crib**/*Bild, Kindlein in Krippe*	2¼ x 3″	CN
139	**Wall Plaque, Flitting Butterfly**/*Wandring, Sitzendes Kind mit Schmetterling*	2½ x 2½″	OE
140	**Wall Plaque, The mail is here**/*Bild, Trara—die Post ist da*	4¼ x 6¾″	OE
141 3/0	**Apple Tree Girl**/*Frühling, Mädchen im Baum*	4 to 4¼″	OE
141/I (141)	**Apple Tree Girl**/*Frühling, Mädchen im Baum*	6 to 6¾″	OE
141/V	**Apple Tree Girl**/*Frühling, Mädchen im Baum*	10¼″	OE
141/X	**Apple Tree Girl**/*Frühling, Mädchen im Baum*	32″	OE
142 3/0	**Apple Tree Boy**/*Herbst, Junge im Baum*	4 to 4¼″	OE
142/I (142)	**Apple Tree Boy**/*Herbst, Junge im Baum*	6 to 6⅞″	OE
142/V	**Apple Tree Boy**/*Herbst, Junge im Baum*	10¼″	OE
142/X	**Apple Tree Boy**/*Herbst, Junge im Baum*	30″	OE
143/0	**Boots**/*Meister Wichtig*	5 to 5½″	OE
143/I	**Boots**/*Meister Wichtig*	6½ to 6¾″	OE
143.	**Boots**/*Meister Wichtig*	6¾″	CE
144	**Angelic Song**/*Singendes Kind mit Engelein*	4″	OE
145	**Little Guardian**/*Betendes Kind mit Engelein*	3¾ to 4″	OE
146	**Holy Water Font, Angel Duet**/*Weihkessel, Engelgrüppchen*	3¼ x 4¾″	OE
147	**Holy Water Font, Angel Shrine**/*Weihkessel, Engel*	3 x 5 to 3⅛ x 5½″	OE
148	**Boy from HUM 60/A (66)—as a single figure**/*Junge aus HUM 60/A (66)—als einzelne Figur*		CN
149	**Girl from HUM 60/B (47/0)—as a single figure**/*Mädchen aus HUM 60/B (47/0)—als einzelne Figur*		CN
150 2/0	**Happy Days**/*Hausmusik, Kinderpaar*	4¼″	OE
150/0	**Happy Days**/*Hausmusik, Kinderpaar*	5 to 5¼″	OE
150/I	**Happy Days**/*Hausmusik, Kinderpaar*	6¼ to 6½″	OE
150.	**Happy Days**/*Hausmusik, Kinderpaar*	6¼″	CE
151	**Madonna Holding Child (white overglaze)**/*Sitzende Madonna mit sitzendem Kind (weisse Überglasur)*	12½″	OE
151	**Madonna Holding Child (pastel blue cloak)**/*Sitzende*		

INCISED HUM No.	NAME	SIZES	STATUS
	Madonna mit sitzendem Kind (hellblauer Mantel)	12½"	OE
151	**Madonna Holding Child (dark blue cloak)**/*Sitzende Madonna mit sitzendem Kind (dunkelblauer Mantel)*	12½"	CE
151	**Madonna Holding Child (brown cloak)**/*Sitzende Madonna mit sitzendem Kind (brauner Mantel)*	12½"	CE
151	**Madonna Holding Child (ivory finish)**/*Sitzende Madonna mit sitzendem Kind (elfenbeinerne Überglasur)*	12½"	CE
152/0 A	**Umbrella Boy**/*Geborgen, Junge*	4¾"	OE
152 A	**Umbrella Boy (152 A/II)**/*Geborgen, Junge*	8"	OE
152/0 B	**Umbrella Girl**/*Geborgen, Mädchen*	4¾"	OE
152 B	**Umbrella Girl (152 B/II)**/*Geborgen, Mädchen*	8"	OE
153/0	**Auf Wiedersehen**/*Auf Wiedersehen, Kinderpaar*	5½ to 6"	OE
153/0	**Auf Wiedersehen (Boy with Hat)**/*Auf Wiedersehen, Kinderpaar (Junge mit Hut)*	5¼"	CE
153/I	**Auf Wiedersehen**/*Auf Wiedersehen, Kinderpaar*	6¾ to 7"	OE
153.	**Auf Wiedersehen**/*Auf Wiedersehen, Kinderpaar*	7"	CE
154/0	**Waiter**/*Herr Ober*	6 to 6¼"	OE
154/I	**Waiter**/*Herr Ober*	6½ to 7"	OE
154.	**Waiter**/*Herr Ober*	6½"	CE
155	**Madonna with cloak, sitting with child on her lap**/*Sitzende Madonna mit Mantel und Kind auf der Schoss*		CN
156	**Wall picture with sitting woman and child**/*Bild mit sitzender Frau und Kind*		CN
157	**Boy standing with flower basket**/*Stehender Junge mit Blumenkorb*		CN
158	**Girl standing with dog in her arms**/*Stehendes Mädchen mit Hund in ihren Armen*		CN
159	**Girl standing with flowers in her arms**/*Stehendes Mädchen mit Blumen in ihren Armen*		CN
160	**Girl standing in tiered dress and bouquet of flowers**/*Stehendes Mädchen mit Ballkleid und Blumenstrauss*		CN
161	**Girl standing with hands in her pockets**/*Stehendes Mädchen mit Händen in der Tasche*		CN
162	**Girl standing with pocket-book (handbag)**/*Stehendes Mädchen mit Handtasche*		CN
163	**Whitsuntide**/*Glockenturm mit Engeln*	6½ to 7"	OE
164	**Holy Water Font, Worship**/*Weihkessel, Am Wegesrand*	3¼ x 5"	OE
165	**Wall Plaque, Swaying Lullaby**/*Kind mit Hängematte und Vögel, Wandring*	4½ x 5¼"	OE
166	**Boy with Bird, Ashtray**/*Ascher, Junge mit Vogel*	3¼ x 6"	OE
167	**Holy Water Font, Angel with Bird**/*Weihkessel, Sitzender Engel mit Vogel*	3¼ x 4⅛"	OE
168	**Wall Plaque, Standing Boy**/*Bild, Stehender Junge mit Herz und Flasche*	4⅛ x 5½"	OE
169	**Bird Duet**/*Frühlingslied*	3¾ to 4"	OE
170/I	**School Boys**/*Schwieriges Problem*	7¼ to 7½"	OE
170/III	**School Boys**/*Schwieriges Problem*	10 to 10¼"	OE
170	**School Boys**/*Schwieriges Problem*	10"	CE
171	**Little Sweeper**/*Kehrliesl*	4¼"	OE
172/0	**Festival Harmony (Mandolin)**/*Adventsengel mit Mandoline*	8"	OE
172/II	**Festival Harmony (Mandolin)**/*Adventsengel mit Mandoline*	10¼ to 10¾"	OE
172	**Festival Harmony (Mandolin)**/*Adventsengel mit Mandoline*	10¾"	CE
173/0	**Festival Harmony (Flute)**/*Adventsengel mit Flöte*	8"	OE
173/II	**Festival Harmony (Flute)**/*Adventsengel mit Flöte*	10¼ to 11"	OE
173	**Festival Harmony (Flute)**/*Adventsengel mit Flöte*	11"	CE
174	**She Loves Me, She Loves Me Not!**/*Liebt mich, liebt mich nicht!*	4¼"	OE
175	**Mother's Darling**/*Markt-Christel*	5½"	OE
176/0	**Happy Birthday**/*Gratulanten*	5 to 5¼"	OE
176/I	**Happy Birthday**/*Gratulanten*	5¾ to 6"	OE
176.	**Happy Birthday**/*Gratulanten*	5½"	CE
177/I	**School Girls**/*s' Meisterstück*	7½"	OE
177/III	**School Girls**/*s' Meisterstück*	9½"	OE
177	**School Girls**/*s' Meisterstück*	9½"	CE

INCISED HUM No.	NAME	SIZES	STATUS
178	**Photographer**/*Der Fotograf*	4¾ to 5¼"	**OE**
179	**Coquettes**/*Zaungäste*	5 to 5¼"	**OE**
180	**Tuneful Good Night, Wall Plaque**/*Wandschmuck in Herzform, sitzendes Kind mit Trompete*	5 x 4¾"	**OE**
181	**Old Man reading newspaper**/*Opa liest die Zeitung*	6¾"	**CN**
182	**Good Friends**/*Mädchen mit Böckchen*	4 to 4¼"	**OE**
183	**Forest Shrine**/*Waldandacht, Marterl*	9"	**OE**
184	**Latest News**/*Das Allerneueste*	5 to 5¼"	**OE**
185	**Accordion Boy**/*Bandoneonspieler*	5 to 6"	**OE**
186	**Sweet Music**/*Zum Tanz*	5 to 5½"	**OE**
187	**"M.I. Hummel" Store Plaque (English)**/*"M.I. Hummel" Reklame-Schild (auf Englisch)*	5½ x 4"	**OE**
187 A	**"M. I. Hummel" Display Plaque (English)**/*"M.I. Hummel" Reklame-Schild (auf Englisch)*	5½ x 4"	**OE**
188	**Celestial Musician**/*Himmlische Klänge*	7"	**OE**
189	**Old Woman knitting**/*Die alte Strickerin*	6¾"	**CN**
190	**Old Woman to market**/*Oma geht auf den Markt*	6¾"	**CN**
191	**Old Man to market**/*Opa geht auf den Markt*	6¾"	**CN**
192	**Candlelight, Candle Holder**/*Engel mit Kerze, Leuchter*	6¾ to 7"	**OE**
193	**Angel Duet, Candle Holder**/*Stille Nacht, Engelgrüppchen, Leuchter*	5"	**OE**
194	**Watchful Angel**/*Schutzengel*	6¼ to 6¾"	**OE**
195 2/0	**Barnyard Hero**/*Angsthase*	3¾ to 4"	**OE**
195/I	**Barnyard Hero**/*Angsthase*	5½"	**OE**
195.	**Barnyard Hero**/*Angsthase*	5¾ to 6"	**CE**
196/0	**Telling Her Secret**/*Das Geheimnis*	5 to 5½"	**OE**
196/I	**Telling Her Secret**/*Das Geheimnis*	6½ to 6¾"	**OE**
196.	**Telling Her Secret**/*Das Geheimnis*	6¾"	**CE**
197 2/0	**Be Patient**/*Entenmütterchen*	4¼ to 4½"	**OE**
197/I	**Be Patient**/*Entenmütterchen*	6 to 6¼"	**OE**
197.	**Be Patient**/*Entenmütterchen*	6¼"	**CE**
198 2/0	**Home From Market**/*Glück auf, Junge mit Schweinchen im Korb*	4½ to 4¾"	**OE**
198/I	**Home From Market**/*Glück auf, Junge mit Schweinchen im Korb*	5½"	**OE**
198.	**Home From Market**/*Glück auf, Junge mit Schweinchen im Korb*	5¾ to 6"	**CE**
199/0	**Feeding Time**/*Im Hühnerhof*	4¼ to 4½"	**OE**
199/I	**Feeding Time**/*Im Hühnerhof*	5½ to 5¾"	**OE**
199.	**Feeding Time**/*Im Hühnerhof*	5¾"	**CE**
200/0	**Little Goat Herder**/*Ziegenbub*	4½ to 4¾"	**OE**
200/I	**Little Goat Herder**/*Ziegenbub*	5 to 5½"	**OE**
200	**Little Goat Herder**/*Ziegenbub*	5½ to 5¾"	**CE**
201 2/0	**Retreat to Safety**/*In tausend Ängsten*	3¾ to 4"	**OE**
201/I	**Retreat to Safety**/*In tausend Ängsten*	5½ to 5¾"	**OE**
201	**Retreat to Safety**/*In tausend Ängsten*	5¾ to 6"	**CE**
202	**Table Lamp, Old Man reading newspaper**/*Lampenfuss, Opa liest die Zeitung*		**CN**
203 2/0	**Signs of Spring**/*Frühlingsidyll*	4"	**OE**
203/I	**Signs of Spring**/*Frühlingsidyll*	5 to 5½"	**OE**
203	**Signs of Spring**/*Frühlingsidyll*	5¼"	**CE**
204	**Weary Wanderer**/*In Lauterbach hab i...,*	5½ to 6"	**OE**
205	**"M.I. Hummel" Store Plaque (German)**/*"M.I. Hummel," Reklame-Schild (auf Deutsch)*	5½ x 4¼"	**CE**
206	**Holy Water Font, Angel Cloud**/*Weihkessel, Kind auf Wolke*	3¼ x 4¾"	**OE**
207	**Holy Water Font, Heavenly Angel**/*Weihkessel, Christkindlein kommt, Engel*	3 x 5"	**OE**
208	**"M.I. Hummel" Store Plaque (French)**/*"M.I. Hummel" Reklame-Schild (auf Französich)*	5½ x 4"	**CE**
209	**"M. I. Hummel" Store Plaque (Swedish)**/*"M.I. Hummel" Reklame-Schild (auf Schwedisch)*	5½x4"	**CE**
210	**"M.I. Hummel" Store Plaque (Schmid)**/*"M.I. Hummel" Reklame-Schild (Schmid)*	5½ x 4"	**CE**
211	**"M.I. Hummel" Store Plaque (Oeslau)**/*"M.I. Hummel" Reklame-Schild (Oeslau)*	5½ x 4"	**CE**
212	**"Hummel" Orchestra**/*"Hummel" Kapelle*		**CN**

INCISED HUM No.	NAME	SIZES	STATUS
213	"M.I. Hummel" Store Plaque (Spanish)/*"M.I. Hummel" Reklame-Schild (auf Spanisch)*	5¾ x 4¼"	CE
214	Nativity set with wooden stable/*Krippensatz mit Holzstall*		OE
214 A	Virgin Mary and Infant Jesus/*Heilige Jungfrau und Jesuskind*	6½"	CE
214/A	Virgin Mary/*Heilige Jungfrau*	6¼ to 6½"	OE
214/A	Infant Jesus/*Jesuskind*	1½ x 3½"	OE
214 B	Joseph/*Josef*	7½"	OE
214/C	Angel, standing "Good Night"/*Stehender Engel, Angenehme Ruhe*	3½"	OE
214/D	Angel, kneeling "Angel Serenade"/*Fromme Weisen, kniender Engel*	3"	OE
214/E	"We Congratulate"/*Wir gratulieren*	3¾"	OE
214/F	Shepherd, standing with sheep/*Stehender Hirt mit Schafen*	7"	OE
214/G	Shepherd, kneeling/*Kniender Hirtenbub*	5"	OE
214/H	Shepherd Boy, kneeling with flute "Little Tooter"/*Kniender Hirt mit Flöte, Schäferbub*	3¾ to 4"	OE
214/J	Donkey/*Esel*	5"	OE
214/K	Ox (cow)/*Ochse (Kuh)*	3½ x 6¼"	OE
214/L	Moorish King, standing/*Stehender Mohrenkönig*	8 to 8¼"	OE
214/M	King, kneeling on one knee/*Kniender König, auf einem Knie*	5½"	OE
214/N	King, kneeling, with cash-box/*Kniender König, mit Schattulle*	5½"	OE
214/O	Lamb/*Lamm*	1¾ x 2½"	OE
215	Child Jesus, standing with lamb in arms/*Stehendes Christkindlein mit Lamm in den Armen*		CN
216	Joyful, Ashtray, without rest for cigarette/*Gesangsprobe, Ascher ohne Zigarettenablage*		CN
217	Boy with Toothache/*Schmerz lass nach*	5¼ to 5½"	OE
218 2/0	Birthday Serenade/*Geburtstagsständchen*	4¼ to 4½"	OE
218 2/0	Birthday Serenade (Girl playing Accordion)/*Geburtstagsständchen (Mädchen mit Bandoneon)*	4¼ to 4½"	CE
218/0	Birthday Serenade/*Geburtstagsständchen*	5¼"	OE
218/0	Birthday Serenade (Girl playing Accordion)/*Geburtstagsständchen (Mädchen mit Bandoneon)*	5¼"	CE
218	Birthday Serenade (Girl playing Accordion)/*Geburtstagsständchen (Mädchen mit Bandoneon)*	5¼"	CE
219/2/0	Little Velma/*Die kleine Velma*	4"	CN
220	We Congratulate (with base)/*Pärchen (mit Fuss)*	3¾ to 4"	OE
220 2/0	We Congratulate (with base)/*Pärchen (mit Fuss)*	4"	CE
221	Happy Pastime, candy jar/*Strickliesel, Dose*		CN
222	Madonna Plaque with metal frame/*Madonnenbild mit Metallrahmen*	4 x 5"	CE
223	Table Lamp, To Market/*Lampenfuss, Brüderlein und Schwesterlein*	9½"	OE
224/I	Table Lamp, Wayside Harmony/*Lampenfuss, Vaters G'scheitester*	7½"	OE
224/II	Table Lamp, Wayside Harmony/*Lampenfuss, Vaters G'scheitester*	9½"	OE
224	Table Lamp, Wayside Harmony/*Lampenfuss, Vaters G'scheitester*	9½"	CE
225/I	Table Lamp, Just Resting/*Lampenfuss, Mutters Liebste*	7½"	OE
225/II	Table Lamp, Just Resting/*Lampenfuss, Mutters Liebste*	9½"	OE
225	Table Lamp, Just Resting/*Lampenfuss, Mutters Liebste*	9½"	CE
226	The mail is here/*Trara—die Post ist da*	4¼ x 6 to 4½ x 6¼"	OE
227	Table Lamp, She loves me, she loves me not!/*Lampenfuss, Liebt mich, liebt mich nicht!*	7½"	OE
228	Table Lamp, Good Friends/*Lampenfuss, Mädchen mit Böckchen*	7½"	OE
229	Table Lamp, Apple Tree Girl/*Lampenfuss, Frühling, Mädchen im Baum*	7½"	OE
230	Table Lamp, Apple Tree Boy/*Lampenfuss, Herbst, Junge im Baum*	7½"	OE
231	Table Lamp, Birthday Serenade/*Lampenfuss, Geburtstagsständchen*	9¾"	OE
231	Table lamp, Birthday Serenade (Girl playing Accordion)/*Lampenfuss, Geburtstagsständchen (Mädchen mit Bandoneon)*	9¾"	CE
232	Table Lamp, Happy Days/*Lampenfuss, Hausmusik, Kinderpaar*	9¾"	OE
233	Boy Feeding Birds/*Der Tierfreund*		CN
234	Table Lamp, Birthday Serenade/*Lampenfuss, Geburtstagsständchen*	7¾"	OE
234	Table Lamp, Birthday Serenade (Girl playing Accordion)/*Lampenfuss, Geburtstagsständchen (Mädchen mit Bandoneon)*	7¾"	CE
235	Table Lamp, Happy Days/*Lampenfuss, Geburtstagsständchen*	7¾"	OE
236	No Information Available		ON

INCISED HUM No.	NAME	SIZES	STATUS
237	**Wall Plaque, Star Gazer**/*Bild, Sterngucker*	4¾ x 5″	CN
238 A	**Angel with Lute**/*Engel mit Laute*	2 to 2½″	OE
238 B	**Angel with Accordion**/*Engel mit Bandoneon*	2 to 2½″	OE
238 C	**Angel with Trumpet**/*Engel mit Trompete*	2 to 2½″	OE
239 A	**Girl with nosegay**/*Mädchen mit Blumenstrauss*	3½″	OE
239 B	**Girl with doll**/*Mädchen mit Puppe*	3½″	OE
239 C	**Boy with horse**/*Junge mit Holzpferd*	3½″	OE
240	**Little Drummer**/*Trommler*	4 to 4¼″	OE
241	**Holy Water Font, Angel, Joyous News with Lute**/*Weihkessel, Adventsengelchen mit Laute*		CN
241	**Angel Lights, Candle Holder**/*Leuchter, Engelbrücke*	10⅓ x 8⅓″	OE
242	**Holy Water Font, Angel, Joyous News with Trumpet**/*Weihkessel, Adventsengelchen mit Trompete*		CN
243	**Holy Water Font, Madonna and Child**/*Weihkessel, Madonna und Kind*	3⅛ x 4″	OE
244	**No Information Available**		ON
245	**No Information Available**		ON
246	**Holy Water Font, Holy Family**/*Weihkessel, Heilige Familie*	3⅛ x 4½″	OE
247	**Standing Madonna with Child**/*Stehende Madonna mit Kind*	13″	CN
248	**Holy Water Font, Guardian Angel**/*Weihkessel, Schutzengel*	2¼ x 5½″	OE
248/0	**Holy Water Font, Guardian Angel**/*Weihkessel, Schutzengel*	2⅜ x 5⅜″	CE
248/I	**Holy Water Font, Guardian Angel**/*Weihkessel, Schutzengel*	2¾ x 6¼″	CE
249	**Madonna and Child (in relief) (48/V)**/*Madonna und Kind (Relief)*	6¾ x 8¾″	CN
250 A	**Book End, Little Goat Herder**/*Buchstütze, Ziegenbub*	5½″	OE
250 B	**Book End, Feeding Time**/*Buchstütze, Im Hühnerhof*	5½″	OE
251 A	**Book End, Good Friends**/*Buchstütze, Freunde*	5″	OE
251 B	**Book End, She loves me, she loves me not!**/*Buchstütze, Liebt mich, liebt mich nicht!*	5″	OE
252 A	**Book End, Apple Tree Girl**/*Buchstütze, Frühling, Mädchen im Baum*	5″	OE
252 B	**Book End, Apple Tree Boy**/*Buchstütze, Herbst, Junge im Baum*	5″	OE
253	**Girl with basket from HUM 52 (Going to Grandma's)**/*Mädchen mit Korb aus HUM 52 (Hausmütterchen)*	4½″	CN
254	**Girl playing mandolin from HUM 150 (Happy Days)**/*Mädchen mit Mandoline aus HUM 150 (Hausmusik, Kinderpaar)*	4¼″	CN
255	**Stitch in time**/*Zwei rechts—zwei links*	6½ to 6¾″	OE
256	**Knitting Lesson**/*Ob's gelingt?*	7½″	OE
257	**For Mother**/*Fürs Mütterchen*	5 to 5¼″	OE
258	**Which Hand?**/*Rat mal!*	5¼ to 5½″	OE
259	**Girl playing accordion from HUM 218 (Birthday Serenade)**/*Mädchen mit Bandoneon aus HUM 218 (Geburtstagsständchen)*	4″	CN
260	**Large nativity set with wooden stable**/*Krippensatz, gross mit Holzstall*		OE
260 A	**Madonna**/*Madonna*	9¾″	OE
260 B	**Saint Joseph**/*Heiliger Josef*	11¾″	OE
260 C	**Infant Jesus**/*Jesuskind*	5¾″	OE
260 D	**Good Night**/*Angenehme Ruhe*	5¼″	OE
260 E	**Angel Serenade**/*Fromme Weisen*	4¼″	OE
260 F	**We Congratulate**/*Wir gratulieren*	6¼″	OE
260 G	**Shepherd, standing**/*Stehender Hirt*	11¾″	OE
260 H	**Sheep standing with lamb**/*Stehendes Schaf mit Lamm*	3¾″	OE
260 J	**Shepherd Boy, kneeling**/*Kniender Hirtenbub*	7″	OE
260 K	**Little Tooter**/*Schäferbub*	5⅛″	OE
260 L	**Donkey, standing**/*Stehender Esel*	7½″·	OE
260 M	**Cow, lying**/*Liegende Kuh*	6 x 11″	OE
260 N	**Moorish King, standing**/*Stehender Mohrenkönig*	12¾″	OE
260 O	**King, standing**/*Stehender König*	12″	OE
260 P	**King, kneeling**/*Kniender König*	9″	OE
260 R	**One Sheep, lying**/*Liegendes Schaf*	3¼ x 4″	OE
261	**Angel Duet (without Candle Holder)**/*Stille Nacht (ohne Kerzentülle)*	5″	OE
262	**Heavenly Lullaby**/*Wiegenlied (ohne Kerzentülle)*	3½ x 5″	OE
263	**Wall Plaque, Merry Wanderer (in relief)**/*Bild, Wanderbub ohne Hund (Relief)*	4 x 5¾″	CN
264	**Annual Plate, 1971, Heavenly Angel**/*Jahresteller, 1971, Christkindlein kommt, Engel*	7½″	CE

INCISED HUM No.	NAME	SIZES	STATUS
265	**Annual Plate, 1972, Hear Ye, Hear Ye**/*Jahresteller, 1972, Hört Ihr Leute, Nachtwächter*	7½″	CE
266	**Annual Plate, 1973, Globe Trotter**/*Jahresteller, 1973, Hinaus in die Ferne*	7½″	CE
267	**Annual Plate, 1974, Goose Girl**/*Jahresteller, 1974, Gänseliesl*	7½″	CE
268	**Annual Plate, 1975, Ride into Christmas**/*Jahresteller, 1975, Fahrt in die Weihnacht*	7½″	CE
269	**Annual Plate, 1976, Apple Tree Girl**/*Jahresteller, 1976, Frühling, Mädchen im Baum*	7½″	CE
270	**Annual Plate, 1977, Apple Tree Boy**/*Jahresteller, 1977, Herbst, Junge im Baum*	7½″	CE
271	**Annual Plate, 1978, Happy Pastime**/*Jahresteller, 1978, Strickliesl*	7½″	CE
272	**Annual Plate, 1979, Singing Lesson**/*Jahresteller, 1979, 's stimmt net*	7½″	OE
273	**Annual Plate, 1980, School Girl**/*Jahresteller, 1980, Erster Schulgang*	7½″	ON
274	**Annual Plate, 1981, Umbrella Boy**/*Jahresteller, 1981, Geborgen, Junge*	7½″	ON
275	**Annual Plate, 1982, Umbrella Girl**/*Jahresteller, 1982, Geborgen, Mädchen*	7½″	ON
276	**Annual Plate, 1983, Postman**/*Jahresteller, 1983, Eilbote*	7½″	ON
277	**Annual Plate, 1984, Little Helper**/*Jahresteller, 1984, Fleissiges Lieschen*	7½″	ON
278	**Annual Plate, 1985, Chick Girl**/*Jahresteller, 1985, Kükenmütterchen*	7½″	ON
279	**Annual Plate, 1986, Playmates**/*Jahresteller, 1986, Hasenvater*	7½″	ON
280	**Anniversary Plate, 1975, Stormy Weather**/*Jubiläumsteller, 1975, Unter einem Dach*	10″	CE
281	**Anniversary Plate, 1980, Pair of girls from HUM 348 Ring Around the Rosie**/*Jubiläumsteller, Mädchenpaar aus HUM 348 Ringelreihen*	10″	ON
286			ON
287			ON
288			ON
289			ON
290			ON
291			ON
292			ON
293			ON
294			ON
295			ON
296			ON
297			ON
298			ON
299			ON
300	**Bird Watcher**/*Der Tierfreund*	5″	OE
301	**Christmas Angel**/*Der Weihnachtsengel*	6¼″	PFE
302	**Concentration**/*Wie macht sie das nur?*	5″	PFE
303	**Arithmetic Lesson**/*Rechenstunde*	5¼″	PFE
304	**The Artist**/*Kunstmaler*	5½″	OE
305	**The Builder**/*Der Schwerarbeiter*	5½″	OE
306	**Little Bookkeeper**/*Stellvertretung*	4¾″	OE
307	**Good Hunting!**/*Weidmannsheil!*	5″	OE
308	**Little Tailor**/*Schneiderlein*	5¼ to 5¾″	OE
309	**With Loving Greetings**/*Ein dicker Gruss*	3¼″	PFE
310	**Wall Plaque, Searching Angel**/*Bild, Was ist denn da drunten los?*	4¼ x 3¼″	OE
311	**Kiss Me!**/*Hab'mich lieb!*	6 to 6¼″	OE
312	**Honey Lover**/*Honiglecker*	3¾″	PFE
313	**Sunny Morning**/*Sonnenkind*	3¾″	PFE
314	**Confidentially**/*Zwiegespräch*	5¼ to 5¾″	OE
315	**Mountaineer**/*I' hab's erreicht*	5″	OE
316	**Relaxation**/*Eine gute Erholung*	4″	PFE
317	**Not for you!**/*Nix für dich!*	5½″	OE
318	**Art Critic**/*Der Kunstkritiker*	5½″	PFE
319	**Doll Bath**/*Puppenbad*	5″	OE
320	**The Professor**/*Der Professor*	5¾″	PFE
321	**Wash Day**/*Grosse Wäsche*	5½ to 6″	OE
322	**Little Pharmacist**/*Der Apotheker*	5¾ to 6″	OE
323	**Wall Plaque, Merry Christmas**/*Bild, Frohe Weihnachten*	5¼ x 3½″	OE

INCISED HUM No.	NAME	SIZES	STATUS
324	**At the Fence**/*Am Zaun*	4¾″	**PFE**
325	**Helping Mother**/*Mutters grosse Stütze*	5″	**PFE**
326	**Wall Plaque, Being Punished**/*Bild, Junge im Karzer*	4 x 5″	**PFE**
327	**The Run-a-way**/*Der frohe Wanderer*	5¼″	**OE**
328	**Carnival**/*Fastnacht*	5¾ to 6″	**OE**
329	**Off to School**/*Frisch gewagt*	5″	**PFE**
330	**Baking Day**/*Die Bäckerin*	5¼″	**PFE**
331	**Crossroads**/*Am Scheideweg*	6¾″	**OE**
332	**Soldier Boy**/*Still gestanden!*	5¾ to 6″	**OE**
333	**Blessed Event**/*Das grosse Ereignis*	5¼ to 5½″	**OE**
334	**Homeward Bound**/*Heimkehr vom Felde*	5¼″	**OE**
335	**Lucky Boy**/*Der Glücksbub*	5¾ to 6″	**PFE**
336	**Close Harmony**/*Geburtstagsständchen*	5¼ to 5½″	**OE**
337	**Cinderella**/*Aschenputtel*	4½″	**OE**
338	**Birthday Cake**/*Der Geburtstagskuchen*	3¾″	**PFE**
339	**Behave!**/*Wir gehen spazieren*	5⅓ to 5¾″	**PFE**
340	**Letter to Santa Claus**/*Brief ans Christkind*	7¼″	**OE**
341	**Birthday Present**/*Das Geburtstagsgeschenk*	5 to 5⅓″	**PFE**
342	**Mischief Maker**/*Der Störenfried*	5″	**OE**
343	**Christmas Song**/*Weihnachtslied*	6½″	**PFE**
344	**Feathered Friends**/*Schwanenteich*	4¾″	**OE**
345	**A Fair Measure**/*Der Kaufmann*	5½ to 5¾″	**OE**
346	**Smart Little Sister**/*Das kluge Schwesterlein*	4¾″	**OE**
347	**Adventure Bound, The Seven Swabians**/*Die sieben Schwaben*	7½ x 8¼″	**OE**
348	**Ring Around the Rosie**/*Ringelreihen*	6¾″	**OE**
349	**The Florist**/*Der Blumenfreund*	7 to 7½″	**PFE**
350	**On Holiday**/*Zum Festtag*	4¼″	**PFE**
351	**The Botanist**/*Enzian-Mädchen*	4 to 4¼″	**PFE**
352	**Sweet Greetings**/*Ein süsser Gruss*	4¼″	**PFE**
353/0	**Spring Dance**/*Sommertanz*	5¼″	**OE**
353/I	**Spring Dance**/*Sommertanz*	6¾″	**OE**
354 A	**Holy Water Font, Angel with Lantern**/*Weihkessel, Engel mit Laterne*	3¼ x 5″	**PFE**
354 B	**Holy Water Font, Angel with Trumpet**/*Weihkessel, Engel mit Trompete*	3¼ x 5″	**PFE**
354 C	**Holy Water Font, Angel with Bird and Cross**/*Weihkessel, Engel mit Kreuz und Vogel*	3¼ x 5″	**PFE**
355	**Autumn Harvest**/*Herbstsegen*	5″	**OE**
356	**Gay Adventure**/*Frohes Wandern*	4¾″	**OE**
357	**Guiding Angel**/*Kniender Engel mit Laterne*	2¾″	**OE**
358	**Shining Light**/*Kniender Engel mit Kerze*	2¾″	**OE**
359	**Tuneful Angel**/*Kniender Engel mit Horn*	2¾″	**OE**
360/A	**Wall Vase, Boy and Girl**/*Wandvase, Junge und Mädchen*	4½ x 6″	**OE**
360/B	**Wall Vase, Boy**/*Wandvase, Junge*	4½ x 6″	**OE**
360/C	**Wall Vase, Girl**/*Wandvase, Mädchen*	4½ x 6″	**OE**
361	**Favorite Pet**/*Ostergruss*	4½″	**OE**
362	**I Forgot**/*Ich hab's vergessen*	5½″	**PFE**
363	**Big Housecleaning**/*Grossreinemachen*	4″	**OE**
364	**Supreme Protection**/*Schutzmantel-Madonna*	8¾ to 9″	**PFE**
365	**Littlest Angel**/*'s Hummele*	2¼ to 2¾″	**PFE**
366	**Flying Angel**/*Hängeengel*	3½″	**OE**
367	**Busy Student**/*Musterschülerin*	4¼″	**OE**
368	**Lute Song**/*Lautenspiel*	5″	**PFE**
369	**Follow the Leader**/*Mach mit*	7″	**OE**
370	**Companions**/*Gratulanten-Muttertag*	4¼ to 4¾″	**PFE**
371	**Daddy's girls**/*Gratulanten-Vatertag*	4¾″	**PFE**
372	**Blessed Mother**/*Mutter Gottes*	10¼″	**PFE**
373	**Just Fishing**/*Der Fischer*	4¼ x 4½″	**PFE**
374	**Lost Stocking**/*Hab mein Strumpf verloren*	4½″	**OE**
375	**Morning Stroll**/*Ausfahrt*	4¼″	**PFE**
376	**Little Nurse**/*"Hänsel, merk dir das"*	4″	**PFE**
377	**Bashful!**/*Vergissmeinnicht*	4¾″	**OE**
378	**Easter Greetings!**/*Ostergruss*	5″	**OE**
379	**Don't be Shy**/*Da, nimm's doch*	4¼ to 4½″	**PFE**

INCISED HUM No.	NAME	SIZES	STATUS
380	**Daisies Don't Tell**/*Er liebt mich*	4½ to 5″	PFE
381	**Flower Vendor**/*Zum Blumenmarkt*	5¼″	OE
382	**Visiting an Invalid**/*Krankenbesuch*	5″	OE
383	**Going Home**/*Wanderfreunde*	4¼ to 4¾″	PFE
384	**Easter Time**/*Osterfreunde*	4″	OE
385	**Chicken-Licken!**/*Kükenliesl*	4¾″	OE
386	**On Secret Path**/*Auf heimlichen Wegen*	5¼″	OE
387	**Valentine Gift**/*Valentinsgeschenk, "I hab di gern"*	5¼″	CE
388	**Candle Holder, Little Band**/*Leuchter, Kindergruppe*	3 x 4¾″	OE
388/M	**Candle Holder on Music Box, Little Band**/*Leuchter, Kindergruppe auf Musikwerk*	3 x 4¾″	OE
389	**Girl with sheet of music**/*Mädchen mit Notenblatt*	2½″	OE
390	**Boy with accordion**/*Junge mit Bandoneon*	2½″	OE
391	**Girl with trumpet**/*Mädchen mit Trompete*	2½″	OE
392	**Little Band (on base)**/*Kindergruppe (auf Fuss)*	3 x 4¾″	OE
392/M	**Little Band on Music Box**/*Kindergruppe auf Musikwerk*	3 x 4¾″	OE
393	**Holy Water Font, Dove**/*Weihkessel, Taube*	2¾ x 4¼″	PFE
394	**Timid Little Sister**/*Das ängstliche Schwesterlein*	6½″	PFE
395	**Shepherd Boy**/*Hirtenbub*	6 to 6½″	PFE
396	**Ride into Christmas**/*Fahrt in die Weihnacht*	5¾″	OE
690	**Smiling Through, Goebel Collectors' Club Plaque**/*Immer froh, Bild*	5¾″	OE
700	**Annual Bell 1978, Let's Sing**/*Jahresglocke 1978, Heini, Bandoneonspieler*	6″	CE
701	**Annual Bell 1979, Farewell**/*Jahresglocke 1979, Auf Wiedersehen*	6″	OE

Many collectors are interested in the trade marks that were used on "M.I. HUMMEL" figurines; therefore, we have used the numbering system of

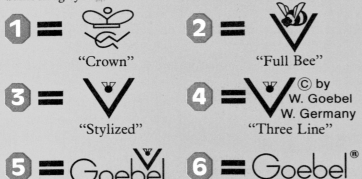

1 = "Crown"

2 = "Full Bee"

3 = "Stylized"

4 = © by W. Goebel W. Germany "Three Line"

5 = Goebel "Goebel Bee"

6 = Goebel® "Current"

to identify each mark that a particular figurine can be found with. There will be some exceptions to this rule. We will list only the marks that were in general circulation of each figurine. For instance, HUM 347 Adventure Bound will be listed as only 4, 5 and 6 trademarks, as it was first sold in the U.S. market in 1971. We have, however, in our collection, an early sample model with a "full bee" trademark. This would be extremely rare, and would not be listed. Some early figurines will be found with no trademark at all. This fact does not lessen their value to any great extent, but does make it more difficult to determine their age. Where figurines vary greatly in size, we will use the "bracket" system, showing the smallest to the largest size, i.e. 5½″ to 6″. Your measurement may vary depending on what means you use to measure. To properly measure a figurine, you should place it on a flat surface, then stand a ruler beside it. Place another ruler or straight object horizontally touching the highest point of the figurine and the perpendicular ruler. You will then have an accurate measurement.

Decoration-designators for "M.I. Hummel" figurines

All "M.I. Hummel" figurines are handpainted according to "M.I. Hummel's" original design. The decoration techniques had to be numbered because the factory uses so many.

The "M.I. Hummel" decor is done in painting method number eleven. A stroke-eleven (/11) is added to the model number following the size indicator in the factory's literature and price lists. *It does not, however, appear incised on the base.* In this book we only refer to incised numbers.

With the exception of madonnas and some other religious items, the decor-indicator was dropped where pieces are produced in only one authorized color variation. The religious items, though, were made in authentic color variations listed below:

Decor No.	Marked	Description
11	/11	all matte-finish colors in a rich variety of pastels inspired by rural surroundings.
11 blue	/11 blue	madonna with dark blue cloak; rest of figurine in pastels.
13	/13	ivory decoration in pastels.
6 blue	/6 blue	madonna with pastel blue cloak; rest of figurine in matching pastels.
6 red	/6 red	madonna with light red cloak; rest of figurine in matching pastels.
83	/83	matte-finish shading on bisque body.
H	/H	brown matte decor, very rare—not made after 1955.
W	/W	white overglaze.

Puppy Love
  HUM 1........5″ to 5¼″
  ①②③④⑤⑥
Early models were made with
the head at different angle and
without tie.

HUM 1   Puppy Love

Little Fiddler
   HUM 2/0 . . . . . . 5¾″ to 6½″
      2/I . . . . . . 7½″
      2/II . . . . . 10¾″
      2/III . . . . 12¼″
      (2/3)
      ①②③④⑤⑥
Many size variations. Always with brown hat. Restyled in 1972 in size 2/II, and 1978 in size 2/I. Old name "Violinist" or "The Wandering Fiddler". Same as HUM 4 except color of hat.

Book Worm
   HUM 3/I . . . . . . 5½″
      3/II
      (3/2) . . . . 8″
      3/III
      (3/3) . . . . 9″ to 9½″
      ①②③④⑤⑥
Old name, "Little Book Worm". Same as HUM 8

Little Fiddler
   HUM 4 . . . . 4¾″ to 5¾″
      ①②③④⑤⑥
Same as HUM 2 except it has black hat. Many size variations. Old name, "Violinist" or "The Wandering Fiddler".

Strolling Along
   HUM 5 . . . . 4¾″ to 5¼″
      ①②③④⑤⑥
Older models have eyes that glance off to one side. Newer models look straight ahead. Color of dog will vary.

HUM 2   Little Fiddler

HUM 3   Book Worm

HUM 4   **Little Fiddler**   Notice great variation in sizes

HUM 5   **Strolling Along**   Newer model

Sensitive Hunter
HUM 6/0 . . . . . . 4¾"
6/I . . . . . . 5½"
6/II . . . . 7 to 7½"
6 . . . . 5" (CE)
①②③④⑤⑥
Old name, "The Timid Hunter". Lederhosen straps on older models are parallel in back. Newer model has crossed-strap suspenders.

Merry Wanderer
HUM 7/0 . . . . . . 6" to 6¼"
7/I . . . . . . 7" to 8"
7/II
(7/2) . . . . 9½" to 10"
7/III . . . . 11" to 12"
7/X . . . . . 32"
①②③④⑤⑥
More size variations than any other figurine. Restyled in size 7/II with new textured finish in 1972, with incised copyright date. Size 7/III restyled in 1978 but without an incised copyright date. Older models of size 7/I have what collectors call a "double base".

Book Worm
HUM 8 . . . . 4" to 4½"
①②③④⑤⑥
Same as HUM 3 except smaller in size. Old name, "Little Book Worm".

Begging his Share
HUM 9 . . . . 5¼" to 5¾"
①②③④⑤⑥
Many size variations. Until 1964 made with hole for candle in center of cake; later models have solid cake.

HUM 6 **Sensitive Hunter**

HUM 6 Old style and New style

HUM 7   Merry Wanderer

HUM 8   Book Worm

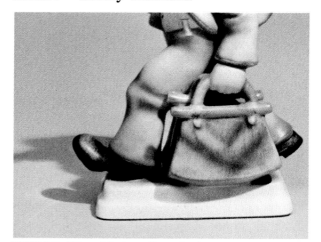

HUM 7 "Double base" variation on old style HUM 7/I

HUM 9   Begging his Share Current model on left, old "Full Bee" on right

HUM 10　Old 10/3　　　New 10/III　　　Old 10/I　　　New 10/I

Flower Madonna
　　HUM 10/I . . . . . 7¾″ to 9½″
　　10/III
　　(10/3). . . . 11″ to 13″
　　①②③④⑤⑥

First created in 1935 by modeller Rinehold Unger according to the original drawing of Sister M.I. Hummel. In 1956 the mold was renewed (restyled) and made approximately 2 inches smaller. The halo was changed at that time from the open style to the flat style. It has been produced in white overglaze, pastel blue cloak, brown cloak, ivory cloak and pastel yellow. Only the pastel blue and the white overglaze are produced today. Old catalogues list it as large as 14 inches. Some early models appear with only the number 10 (no size designator). Also called "Sitting Madonna with Child" in old catalogues.

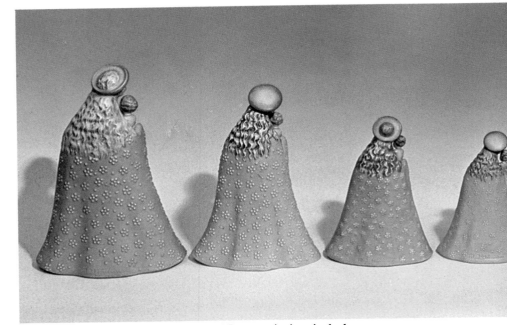

HUM 10　**Flower Madonna**　Note variation in halo

HUM 10   Ivory finish   Brown finish   Pastel Blue finish

Merry Wanderer

    HUM 11 2/0. . . . 4¼″ to 4½″
         11/0 . . . . . 4¾″ to 5″
         11. . . . . . 4¾″ (CE)
        ❶❷❸❹❺❻

Same as HUM 7

Chimney Sweep

    HUM 12 2/0. . . . 4″ to 4¼″
         12/I . . . . . 5½″ to 6½″
         12. . . 6″ to 6¼″ (CE)
        ❶❷❸❹❺❻

Old name, 'Smoky" or "Good Luck".

Meditation

    HUM 13/2/0 . . . 4¼″
         13/0 . . . . . 5″ to 6″
         13/II
         (13/2). . . . 7″ to 7¼″
         13/V
         (13/5) . .13½″ to 14″
        ❶❷❸❹❺❻

Size 13/2 has flowers in back half of basket. Restyled in 1978 with no flowers in basket. Size 13/V has full basket of flowers. (See dust jacket of this volume for picture.) Slight variations in hair ribbons on older models of 13/0. A 1962 copyright date appears on newer models of size 13/2/0. Also called "The Little Messenger".

HUM 11 Merry Wanderer

HUM 12   Chimney Sweep

HUM 13   Meditation   13/II New   13/2 Old

**Book Worm, Book Ends,
Boy and Girl**
   HUM 14 A&B . . 5½″
   ①②③④⑤⑥
Old name "Sitting Boy and
Girl" Book Ends. These figurines are weighted with sand
through a hole on the bottom
and closed with a plastic or cork
plug. Sometimes sealed with a
paper sticker with inscription
"75 Years Goebel". The girl is
the same as HUM 3 and HUM
8 except that pictures on book
are black and white rather than
in color. The boy is only made
as part of book end set and not
sold separately.

Hear Ye, Hear Ye
   HUM 15/0 . . . . . 5″ to 5¼″
   15/I . . . . . 6″ to 6¼″
   15/II
   (15/2) . . . . 7″ to 7½″
   ①②③④⑤⑥
Old name "Night Watchman".
Some variation in color of mit-
tens. Right hand shows fingers
on older models.

Little Hiker
   HUM 16 2/0 . . . . 3¾″ to 4¼″
   16/I . . . . . 5½″ to 6″
   16. . 5½″ to 5¾″ (CE)
   ①②③④⑤⑥
Old name, "Happy-Go-
Lucky".

HUM 14 A&B   Book Worm, Book Ends, Girl and Boy

Congratulations
   HUM 17 . . . . 6″
   17/0 . . . . . 5½″ to 6″
   (CE)
   17/II
   (17/2) . . . . 7¾″ to
   8¼″ (CE)
   ①②③④⑤⑥
Older models do not have socks.
Restyled in 1971. Larger size
(17/II) is no longer produced.
Extremely rare. Early crown
mark pieces are marked 17 with
either a zero or a 2 directly
underneath. Old catalogue
dated 1955 lists size of 3¾″
which is believed to be in error.
New models have no size designator.

HUM 15 Hear Ye, Hear Ye Old model, left—notice fingers   New model, right

HUM 16 Little Hiker

HUM 17 Congratulations Current production on left

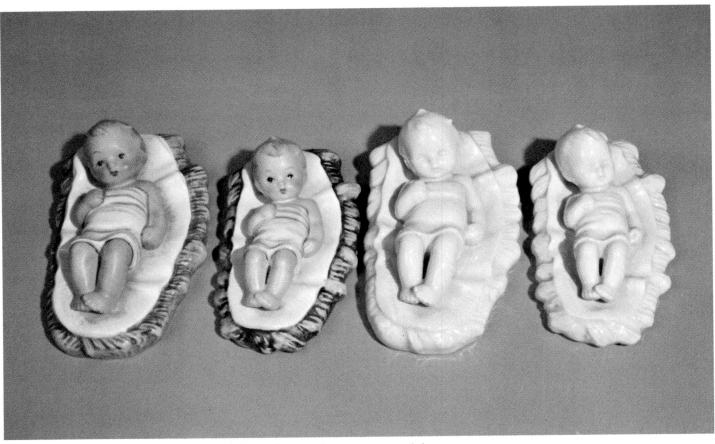

HUM 18   Christ Child   Early models are larger than newer models

Christ Child
HUM 18.......3¼″ x 6″

①②③④⑤⑥

Early models measure 3¾″ x 6½″. Also sold in white over-glaze at one time, extremely rare (CE). Old name "Christmas Night".

Prayer Before Battle on Big Round Tray
HUM 19.......? (CN)

Factory book of models indicates: "Big round tray with praying child (with flag and trumpet) standing at wooden (toy) horse. Prayer Before Battle, modelled by A. Möller—June 20, 1935. An additional note states that this item was not accepted by the Convent at Siessen. No known examples.

Prayer Before Battle
HUM 20.......4″ to 4½″

①②③④⑤⑥

Only slight variations between old and new models.

Heavenly Angel
HUM 21/0.....4″ to 4¾″
21/0 ½ ...5¾″ to 6½″
21/I.....6¾″ to 7¼″
21/II....8½″ to 8¾″

①②③④⑤⑥

Only figurine to have "½" size designator. Many size variations. Old name, "Little Guardian". Also sold in white overglaze at one time. Extremely rare.

Holy Water Font, Sitting Angel
HUM 22/0 ....3″ to 4″
22/I.....3½″ to 4⅞″
22. .....3⅛″ to 4½″
　　　　　　　　(CE)

①②③④⑤⑥

Variations in color and design of bowl.

HUM 21   Heavenly Angel

HUM 20   Prayer Before Battle

HUM 22   Holy Water Font, Sitting Angel

Adoration

HUM 23/I . . . . . 6¼″ to 7″
    23/III
    (23/3) . . . . 8¾″ to 9″
①②③④⑤⑥

Both sizes sold in white overglaze at one time; extremely rare. Old name, "Ave Maria". Size 23/I was restyled in 1978, with new textured finish.

Lullaby, Candle Holder

HUM 24/I . . . . . 3½″ x 5″
              to 5½″
    24/III
    (24/3) . . . . 6¼″ x 8¾″
①②③④⑤⑥

Variations in size and construction of hole for candle on size 24/I. Old name, "Cradle Song". Also made without hole for candle—see HUM 262. Size 24/III had been considered rare but is once again in current production.

Angelic Sleep, Candle Holder

HUM 25 . . . . 3½″ x 5″
              to 5½″
①②③④⑤⑥

Also sold in white overglaze at one time, extremely rare. Some old catalogues and price lists show as size 25/I in error. Made only in one size.

Holy Water Font, Child Jesus

HUM 26/0 . . . . . 2¾″ x 5¼″
    26/I . . . . . 3¼″ x 6″
①②③④⑤⑥

Usually sold in dark red gown. Light blue color rare. Size 26/I has scalloped edge on bowl of font, considered extremely rare.

HUM 23   Adoration

HUM 24   Lullaby, Candle Holder

HUM 25   Angelic Sleep, Candle Holder

HUM 26   Holy Water Font, Child Jesus

Joyous News
> **HUM 27/I . . . . . 2¾"**
> **27/III**
> **(27/3). . . . 4¼" x 4¾"**
> ①②③ ? ⑤⑥

27/I is similar to III/40/I except for location of holder for candle. The small size Joyous News candle holder (27/I) is no longer produced and is considered extremely rare. Joyous News 27/3 in the older trade marks is considered rare.

Wayside Devotion
> **HUM 28/II**
> **(28/2). . . . 7" to 7½"**
> **28/III. . . . 8¾"**
> ①②③④⑤⑥

Old name, "The Little Shepherd". Also sold in white overglaze at one time—extremely rare.

Holy Water Font, Guardian Angel
> **HUM 29. . . . . . 2½" x 5¾"**
> **29/0 . . . . . 2⅞" x 6"**
> **29/I . . . . . 3" x 6⅜"**
> ①②③

(CE) Closed Edition. Redesigned into HUM 248 because of fragile wings.

Ba-Bee-Ring
> **HUM 30 A & B . . 4¾" x 5"**
> **30/0**
> **A & B . . . . 4¾" x 5"**
> **(CE)**
> **30/1**
> **A & B . . . . 5¼" x 6"·**
> **(CE)**
> ①②③④⑤⑥

There is some size variation between old and new pieces. Early red color rings are extremely rare. Now produced in bisque color rings only. Old name, "Hummel Rings". New models have no size designator.

HUM 27   Joyous News   27/I on left   27/3 on right

HUM 28   Wayside Devotion

66

HUM 29 **Holy Water Font, Guardian Angel** 29/0 29. HUM 248

HUM 30 **Ba-Bee-Ring** in red; only known example.

HUM 30 30/0 A 30/1 A

Silent Night with Black Child/Advent Group with Candle

    HUM 31 . . . . 3½″ x 5″
                 (CE)

This is the only piece known to exist today. Similar to HUM 54. Note embossed ear ring and bare feet of black child. Designed in 1935 but not produced in quantity. According to factory representatives, a few HUM 54 may have been produced with a black child, but wearing shoes instead of bare feet.

Little Gabriel

    HUM 32 . . . . 5″
        32/0 . . . . . 5″ to 5½″
               (CE)
        32/I . . . . . 5¾″ to 6″
               (CE)

① ② ③ ④ ⑤ ⑥

Many size variations in this figurine. New model has no size designator.

Ashtray, Joyful

    HUM 33 . . . . 3½″ x 6″

① ② ③ ④ ⑤ ⑥

Older models have slightly different construction of ashtray.

HUM 31   Silent Night with Black Child/Advent Group with Candle

HUM 32   Little Gabriel   32/0   32/0   32/I

HUM 33   Ashtray, Joyful

Ashtray, Singing Lesson
     HUM 34 . . . . 3½″ x 6¼″
          ❶❷❸❹❺❻
Slight variation in colors of older models.

Holy Water Font, The Good Shepherd
     HUM 35/0 . . . . . 2½″ x 4¾″
          35/I . . . . . 2¾″ x 5¾″
          ❶❷❸❹❺❻
Variation in construction of bowl of font.

Holy Water Font, Child with Flowers
     HUM 36/0 . . . . . 3¼″ x 4¼″
          36/I . . . . . 3½″ x 4½″
          36. . . . . . 3½″ x 4½″
               (CE)
          ❶❷❸❹❺❻
Also called "Flower Angel" or "Angel with Flowers".

HUM 34   Ashtray, Singing Lesson

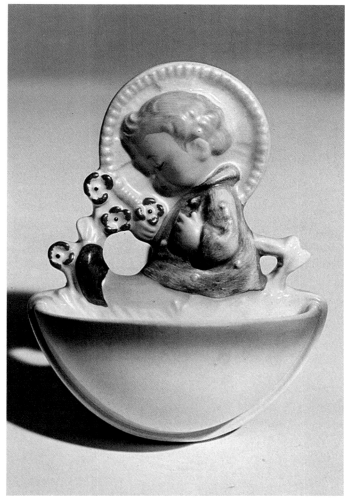

HUM 36   Holy Water Font, Child with Flowers

HUM 35   Holy Water Font, The Good Shepherd

Herald Angels, Candle Holder

　HUM 37. . . . . . . 2¾″ x 4 to
　　　　　　　4½″

①②③④⑤⑥

On older models the candle holder is much taller than on the new ones. The order of placement of the angels may vary on the older models. Current production pieces have a half-inch wider base.

Angel, Joyous News with Lute, Candle Holder

　HUM I/38/0 . . . 2″ to 2¼″
　　III/38/0 . . 2″ to 2¼″
　　III/38/I . . 2¾″

①②③④⑤⑥

Angel, Joyous News with Accordion, Candle Holder

　HUM I/39/0 . . . 2″ to 2¼″
　　III/39/0 . . 2″ to 2¼″
　　III/39/I . . 2¾″

①②③④⑤⑥

Angel, Joyous News with Trumpet, Candle Holder

　HUM I/40/0 . . . 2″ to 2¼″
　　III/40/0 . . 2″ to 2¼″
　　III/40/I . . 2¾″

①②③④⑤⑥

Roman numerals to the left of the HUM number indicate the size of the candle that fits into the figurine. Size I is .6 cm, size III is 1 cm. (Note: Not all figurines which hold candles are photographed with candles in this book, but they are usually sold with candles.) Also called "Little Heavenly Angel" in old catalogues. Also known as "Angel Trio" candle holders. Candle holders are always on right side of angel.

HUM 37　Herald Angels, Candle Holder

Singing Lesson (without base)

　HUM 41. . . . . . . ? (CN)

Factory book of models indicates this piece is similar to HUM 34 (Singing Lesson, Ashtray). Closed 31 October 1935. No known examples.

Good Shepherd

　HUM 42. . . . . . . 6¼″
　　42/0 . . . . . 6¼″ to
　　　　　　　6½″ (CE)
　　42/I . . . . . 7¼″ to
　　　　　　　7¾″ (CE)

①②③④⑤⑥

Size 42/0 with light blue gown considered extremely rare. Size 42/I considered extremely rare. Currently produced without size designator in small size only.

**HUM 38   Angel, Joyous News with Lute, Candle Holder   39   with Accordion, Candle Holder
40   with Trumpet, Candle Holder**

HUM 42   Good Shepherd   42/0   42/I

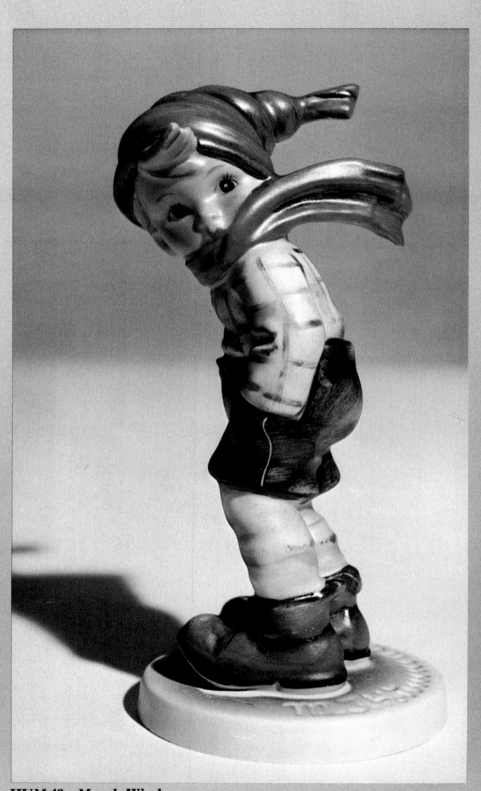

March Winds

HUM 43 . . . . . . 4¾″ to 5½″

①②③④⑤⑥

Many size variations. Older pieces usually larger.

Culprits, Table Lamp

HUM 44 A . . . . . 8½″ to 9½″

①②③④⑤⑥

Older models have a half-inch larger base, and hole for electrical switch on top of base. They usually have a 1935 copyright date incised.

Out of Danger, Table Lamp

HUM 44 B . . . . . 8½″ to 9½″

①②③④⑤⑥

Older models have a half-inch larger base, and hole for electrical switch on top of base. They usually have a 1936 copyright date incised.

HUM 43   March Winds

HUM 44 A   Culprits, Table Lamp   **HUM 44 B   Out of Danger, Table Lamp**

Madonna With Halo
> HUM 45/0 . . . 10½′′′
> 45/I . . . 11½′′ to 13¼′′
> 45/III
> (45/3). . 15½′′ to 16¾′′
> ①②③④⑤⑥

Madonna Without Halo
> HUM 46/0 . . . 10¼′′
> 46/I . . . 11¼′′ to 13′′
> 46/III
> (46/3). . 15¼′′ to 16¼′′
> ①②③④⑤⑥

Many size variations in standing Madonnas. Produced in white overglaze, pastel blue, pastel pink, heavy blue, and ivory finish. Some pieces have been mismarked 45 instead of 46, etc. Some pieces have been discovered with both 45 and 46 on the same piece.

Goose Girl
> HUM 47 3/0 . . 4′′ to 4¼′′
> 47/0 . . . . 4¾′′ to
> 5¼′′
> 47/II
> (47/2). . . 7′′ to 7½′′
> ①②③④⑤⑥

Many size variations. Size 47/II was restyled in early 1970's. Older models of size 47/0 have a blade of grass between the geese.

Madonna Plaque
> HUM 48/0 . . . . 3¼′′x4¼′′
> 48/II
> (48/2). . . 4¾′′x5¾′′
> 48/V
> (48/5). . . 8¾′′x10¾′′
> (CE)
> ①②③④⑤⑥

Also sold in white overglaze at one time, in both 48/0 and 48/II sizes, which are extremely rare. Old crown mark pieces are slightly smaller.

HUM 45   Madonna With Halo   HUM 46   Madonna Without Halo

To Market
> HUM 49 3/0 . . 4′′
> 49/0 . . . . 5′′ to 5½′′
> 49/I . . . . 6¼′′ to 6½′′
> 49 . . . . . . 6¼′′ to 6½′′
> (CE)
> ①②③④⑤⑥

Some newly produced figurines in 6¼′′ size have appeared without a size designator. Only the number 49 is incised on the bottom along with the current trademark. Small 49 3/0 size never has bottle in basket.

HUM 47 Goose Girl

HUM 48 Madonna Plaque

HUM 49 To Market
49/I   49/0   49 3/0

Volunteers
    HUM 50 2/0 . . 4¾″ to 5″
          50/0 . . . . 5½″ to 6″
          50/I . . . . 6½″ to 7″
          50. . . . . 7″ (CE)
          ① ② ③ ④ ⑤ ⑥

Many size variations in older pieces.

Village Boy
    HUM 51 3/0 . . 4″
          51 2/0 . . 5″
          51/0 . . . . 6″ to 6¾″
          51/I . . . . 7¼″ to 8″
          ① ② ③ ④ ⑤ ⑥

Many size variations in older pieces. Some newer models have a 1961 copyright date. Has been slightly restyled several times through the years.

Going to Grandma's
    HUM 52/0 . . . . 4½″ to 5″
          52/I . . . . 6″ to 6¼″
          52. . . . . 6¼″ (CE)
          ① ② ③ ④ ⑤ ⑥

All large size and older small size figurines were produced with a rectangular base. Small size figurines have been produced with an oval base since the early 1960's. The objects protruding from cone represent candy and sweets rather than flowers. The cone appears empty on the large size models.

Joyful
    HUM 53 . . . . . . 3½″ to 4¼″
          ① ② ③ ④ ⑤ ⑥

Many size variations. Older pieces usually larger.

Joyful, Box
    HUM III/53 . . . 6½″
               Bowl Style (CE)
          III/53 . . . 5¾″ **Jar Style**
          ① ② ③ ④ ⑤ ⑥

Bowl style box first produced in 1936. Jar style first produced and sold in 1964.

HUM 50   **Volunteers**   50/0

HUM 51   **Village Boy**   51/0

HUM 52   Going to Grandma's

New—oval style base

Jar style

Bowl style

HUM III/53   Joyful, Box

HUM 53   Joyful

Silent Night, Candle Holder
HUM 54 . . . . . . 3½"x4¾"
①②③④⑤⑥

Older pieces have smaller holes for a candle. There are some color variations in wings of angel. Early crown mark figurines are usually very light in color. A rare variation is with standing child painted as black child—very limited production.

Saint George
HUM 55 . . . . . . 6¾"
①②③④⑤⑥

Old name "Knight St. George" or "St. George and Dragon". Early models had dark red saddle on horse. Have not been able to trace location of Sister M.I. Hummel's original drawing for this figurine. Most likely painted on the wall of a church or religious building.

Culprits
HUM 56/A . . . . 6¼" to 6¾"
①②③④⑤⑥

Variation in height and size of base. Old name, "Apple Thief." Some early crown mark pieces appear with number 56 only. Has been restyled. Older models have the boy's eyes open.

Out Of Danger
HUM 56/B . . . 6¼" to 6¾"
①②③④⑤⑥

Variation in height, and size of base. On older models, the girl's eyes are open; on the newer version her eyes are looking down.

HUM 54   Silent Night, Candle Holder

HUM 55   Saint George

HUM 56/A   Culprits   **HUM 56/B   Out Of Danger**

Bowl style

Jar style

HUM III/57   Chick Girl, Box

Chick Girl
>   **HUM 57/0 . . . . 3½"**
>   **57/I . . . . 4¼"**
>   **57.   . . . . 4" to 4⅜"**
>   **(CE)**

Small size has two chicks in basket. Large size has three chicks. Old name, "The Little Chick Girl." There are three different styles of construction that have been used on bottom of base: quarter, doughnut and plain.

Chick Girl, Box
>   **HUM III/57. . . 6" to 6¼"**
>   **Bowl Style**
>   **(CE)**
>   **III/57. . . 5" Jar**
>   **Style**

Bowl style first produced in 1936. Jar style first produced and sold in 1964.

Playmates
>   **HUM 58/0 . . . . 4"**
>   **58/I . . . . 4¼"**

Some size and color variations between old and new figurines. Both ears of rabbit pointing up on size 58/I. Old name, "Just Friends." Three different styles of construction on bottom of base: quarter, doughnut and plain.

Playmates, Box
>   **HUM III/58. . . 6¾"**
>   **Bowl Style**
>   **(CE)**
>   **III/58. . . 5½"**
>   **Jar Style**

Bowl style first produced in 1936. Jar style first produced and sold in 1964.

HUM 57   Chick Girl   57/I

Skier
>   **HUM 59 . . . . . . 5" to 6"**

Many size variations. Older models sold with wooden ski poles; newer models with plastic or metal.

Jar style

Bowl style

HUM III/58   **Playmates, Box**

HUM 58   **Playmates**   58/I   58/0

HUM 59   **Skier**

Book Ends: Farm Boy
   HUM 60 A.... 4¾″
Book Ends: Goose Girl
   HUM 60 B.... 4¾″
   ①②③④⑤⑥
First produced in September 1936. Trademarks stamped on wood base rather than on figurine.

Book Ends: Playmates
   HUM 61 A.... 4″
Book Ends: Chick Girl
   HUM 61 B.... 4″
   ①②③④⑤⑥
First produced in November 1936. Trademarks stamped on wood base rather than on figurine.

Happy Pastime, Ashtray
   HUM 62...... 3½″x6¼″
   ①②③④⑤⑥
Slight difference in construction of ashtray on older models. Crown mark piece has "M.I. Hummel" signature on back of ashtray. New models have signature on back of girl.

Singing Lesson
   HUM 63...... 2¾″ to 3″
   ①②③④⑤⑥
Some variations in size. Some variations in tilt of boy's head and position of hand. Old name: "Duet".

Singing Lesson, Box
   HUM III/63... 5¾″
                    Bowl Style
                    (CE)
   III/63... 4¾″
                    Jar Style
   ①②③④⑤⑥
Bowl style first produced in 1937. Jar style first produced and sold in 1964. Old name: "Duet" box.

HUM 60 B   Book Ends: Goose Girl   HUM 60 A   Farm Boy

HUM 61 A   Book Ends: Playmates   HUM 61 B   Chick Girl

Shepherd's Boy
   HUM 64...... 5½″ to 6¼″
   ①②③④⑤⑥
Many size variations. Has been restyled with textured finish. Old name is "The Good Shepherd."

HUM 62   Happy Pastime, Ashtray

Jar style   Bowl style

HUM III/63   Singing Lesson, Box

HUM 63   Singing Lesson

HUM 64   Shepherd's Boy   Older model

Farewell

    HUM 65 . . . . . . 4¾″

        65/0 . . . . 4″ (CE)

        65/I . . . . 4½″ to 4⅞″

              (CE)

        65.   . . . . 4¾″ to 5″

              (CE)

①②③④⑤⑥

Many size variations. Has been restyled and numbered 65 only. 65/0 size is extremely rare.

Farm Boy

    HUM 66. . . . . 5″ to 5¾″

①②③④⑤⑥

Many size variations. The old name is "Three Pals."

Doll Mother

    HUM 67 . . . . . . 4¼″ to 4¾″

①②③④⑤⑥

Has been restyled. Slight difference in hair ribbon on girl. Old name is "Little Doll Mother."

Lost Sheep

    HUM 68 2/0 . . 4¼″ to 4½″

        68/0 . . . . 5½″

        68.   . . . . 5½″ to 6½″

              (CE)

①②③④⑤⑥

Older models have dark brown trousers. Has been restyled. Many size variations.

HUM 65   **Farewell**   65/I   65. "Full Bee"

HUM 66   **Farm Boy**

HUM 67   **Doll Mother**   "Full Bee"   "Double Crown"

HUM 68   **Lost Sheep**

      68 2/0   68/0   68. "Crown"   68. "Full Bee"   68. "Double Crown"

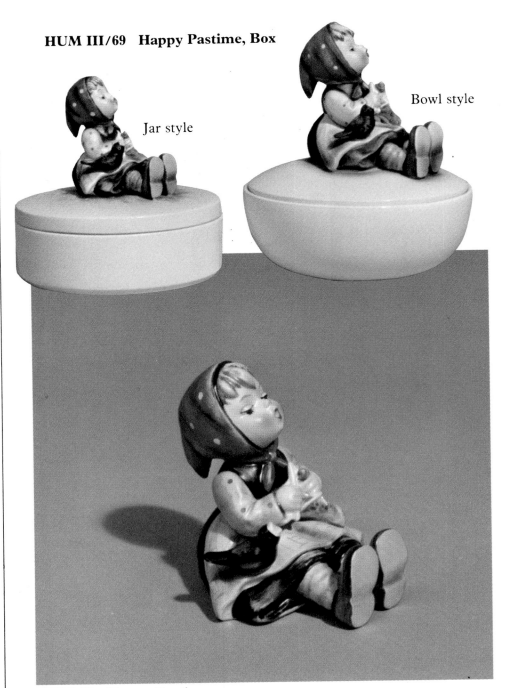

Jar style

Bowl style

HUM 69   Happy Pastime

Happy Pastime
   HUM 69 . . . . . . 3½″
   ①②③④⑤⑥

Very little difference between old and new models. Older models slightly larger.

Happy Pastime, Box
   HUM III/69 . . . 6½″
      Bowl Style
      (CE)
   III/69 . . . 5¼″
      Jar Style
   ①②③④⑤⑥

Bowl style first produced in 1937. Jar style first produced and sold in 1964.

The Holy Child
   HUM 70 . . . . . . 6¾″ to 7½″
   ①②③④⑤⑥

Many size variations. Has been restyled. Newer models have textured finish on gown and robe.

Stormy Weather
   HUM 71 . . . . . . 6″ to 7″
   ①②③④⑤⑥

Many size variations. Has been restyled. Old name "Under One Roof." Slight differences between old and new models. "Full Bee" models are usually the largest in size.

Spring Cheer
   HUM 72 . . . . . . 5″ to 5½″
   ①②③④⑤⑥

Older models have yellow dress and no flowers in right hand. Restyled in the early 1960's. Now with green dress and flowers in both hands. "Crown Mark" pieces have a flower on reverse side. Later production pieces omitted this flower.

HUM 71   Stormy Weather

HUM 72   Spring Cheer

HUM 70   The Holy Child

Little Helper
    HUM 73 . . . . . . 4" to 4½"
    ①②③④⑤⑥

Very little variation between old and new pieces. Older pieces are usually slightly larger. Old name is "Diligent Betsy" or "The Little Sister."

Little Gardener
    HUM 74 . . . . . . 4" to 4½"
    ①②③④⑤⑥

Older models have oval base. Restyled in early 1960's and changed to round base and smaller flower. Many color variations on girl's apron.

Holy Water Font, White Angel
    HUM 75 . . . . . . 3¼"x4½"
    ①②③④⑤⑥

Newer models have hole for hanging font. Variation in construction of bowl. Also called "Angelic Prayer" in some old catalogues.

Book Ends: Doll Mother & Prayer Before Battle
    HUM 76 . . . . . . A & B
                    (CE)

No known examples. Not produced after 28 February 1938.

Holy Water Font, Cross With Doves
    HUM 77 . . . . . . 1¾"x6¼"
                    (CN)

Samples only. Never in production. Edition closed on 21 October 1937.

Infant of Krumbad
    HUM 78/0 . . . . 2¼" (CE)
                    1963
        78/I . . . . 2½"
        78/II . . . 3½"
        78/III
        (78/3) . . . 4½" to 5¼"

(continued)

HUM 73   Little Helper

HUM 74   Little Gardener
   "Crown"   "Crown"   "Full Bee"   "Stylized"

HUM 75   Holy Water Font, White Angel

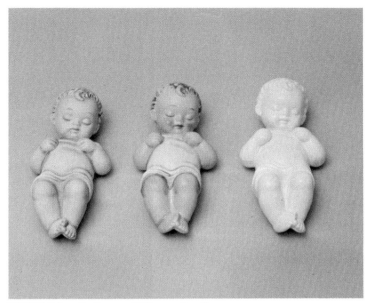

HUM 78   Infant of Krumbad

HUM 77   Holy Water Font, Cross With Doves

HUM 79 rear view

HUM 79   Globe Trotter   New model (left)   Older model (right)

78/V . . . 7½" to 7¾"
78/VI
(78/6). . . 10" to
11¼"
78/VIII . 13¼" to
14¼"
①②③④⑤⑥

Produced in brownish bisque finish (U. S. Market); full color and white overglaze (various other countries). Variation in older models. Restyled in the early 1950's. The two small holes on the back are designed to hold a wire halo. 1966 incised copyright date on some models.

Globe Trotter
HUM 79 . . . . . . 5" to 5¼"
①②③④⑤⑥

Variation in basket weave. The new style is on the left in both photographs. Crown mark pieces usually have tan colored handle on umbrella while others are black. Some variation of color on the inside of basket. Some old catalogues list name as "Happy Traveler." Some older models have dark green hat.

Little Scholar
HUM 80 . . . . . . 5¼" to 5¾"
①②③④⑤⑥

Some color variations. Older models have brown shoes.

School Girl
HUM 81 2/0 . . 4¼" to 4¾"
81/0 . . . . 4¾" to 5¼"
81 . . . . . 5⅛" to 5½"
(CE)
①②③④⑤⑥

Many size variations as well as color variations. Size 81 2/0 basket filled; all others, basket empty. Old catalogue listing of 7¾" is in error.

School Boy
HUM 82 2/0 . . 4" to 4½"
82/0 . . . . 4¾" to 6"
82/II
(82/2) . . . 7½"
①②③④⑤⑥

Many size variations. Old name is "School Days" or "Little Scholar." Size 82/II (82/2) has been considered rare but is once again back in current production.

Angel Serenade
HUM 83 . . . . . . 5½" to 5¾"
①②③④⑤⑥

This figurine had not been produced in quantity since the early 1960's and was considered rare. It is now back on the market with the current trademark. The "Angel Serenade" name is also used for HUM 214/D (part of small Nativity set) and 260/E (part of large Nativity set).

Worship
HUM 84/0 . . . . 5" to 5½"
84/V
**(84/5) . . . 12½" to
13¼"**
84 . . . . . . 5¼" (CE)
①②③④⑤⑥

Size 84/0 also sold in white overglaze at one time; extremely rare. Old name, "At The Wayside." Current models of size 84/V have "M.I. Hummel" signature on back of the shrine. Older models have signature on back of base.

HUM 80   Little Scholar

HUM 81   School Girl

HUM 82   School Boy

HUM 83   Angel Serenade

HUM 84   Worship

Serenade
   HUM 85/0 . . . . 4¾" to 5¼"
   85/II
   (85/2) . . . 7" to 7½"
   ①②③④⑤⑥

Many size variations. Note variation of boy's fingers on flute. Cannot be attributed to any one time period. Old model with "85. 0." number has fingers up. The old name is "The Flutist."

Happiness
   HUM 86 . . . . . . 4½" to 5"
   ①②③④⑤⑥

Many size variations. Old name: "Wandersong."

For Father
   HUM 87 . . . . . . 5½"
   ①②③④⑤⑥

Some size and color variations between old and new models. Old name: "Father's Joy."

HUM 85   Serenade

Hum 85   Serenade Note fingers

HUM 86   Happiness

HUM 87   For Father

Heavenly Protection

HUM 88/I . . . . 6¼″ to 6¾″
    88/II . . . 8¾″ to 9″
    88 . . . . . . 9¼″ (CE)
①②③④⑤⑥

Old name is "Guardian Angel." Some size and color variations between old and new models. Some pieces have 1961 copyright date on bottom.

Little Cellist

HUM 89/I . . . . 5¼″ to 6¼″
    89/II
    (89/2) . . . 7½″ to 7¾″
①②③④⑤⑥

Many size variations. Has been restyled. Older pieces in size 89/I have eyes open looking straight ahead. Newer pieces have eyes looking down. Older pieces have rectangular base. Newer pieces have rectangular base with corners squared off.

Book Ends: Eventide & Adoration (Without Shrine)

HUM 90. . . . . A & B
    (CE)

Factory sample only. Extremely rare. Not produced after 28 February 1938.

Holy Water Font, Angel Facing Left

HUM 91 A . . . . 3⅜″x5″

Holy Water Font, Angel Facing Right

HUM 91 B . . . . 3⅜″x5″

Older models (left) do not have halos while more recent designs have halos and a redesigned water bowl. Trademark, 1, 2, and 3 are without halos, 4, 5 and 6 with halos.

HUM 88 Heavenly Protection 88/I   88/II

HUM 89 Little Cellist
    New model   Old model

HUM 90 Book Ends: (CE) Eventide & Adoration (Without Shrine)

HUM 91 A   Holy Water Font, Angel Facing Left   **HUM 91 B   Angel Facing Right**
Old style   New style

Merry Wanderer, Plaque
HUM 92 . . . . . . 4½"x5" to
5"x5½"

①②③④⑤⑥

Many size variations. Crown mark pieces can be found in both sizes. Some have 1938 copyright date, others do not. Some pieces have "M. I. Hummel" signature on both front and back, while others have signature on back only.

Little Fiddler, Plaque
HUM 93 . . . . . . 4½"x5" to
5"x5½"

①②③④⑤⑥

Many size variations. Two different backgrounds as noted in photograph. Older model (left) extremely rare. Some pieces have "M. I. Hummel" signature on both front and back, while others have signature on back only, or front only. Also sold in white overglaze at one time. The background on the left is similar to HUM 107.

Surprise
HUM 94 3/0 . . 4" to 4¼"
94/I . . . . 5¼" to 5½"
94. . . . . 5¾" (CE)

①②③④⑤⑥

Old name: "The Duet." Older pieces marked "94" or "94/I" have rectangular base. All newer models have oval base. Slight variation in suspender straps on older models.

Brother
HUM 95 . . . . . . 5¼" to 5¾"

①②③④⑤⑥

Many size and color variations. Old name: "Our Hero."

Little Shopper
HUM 96 . . . . . . 4½" to 5"

Many size variations. Old name: "Errand Girl." The old catalogue lists a size 5½". This is believed to be in error.

HUM 92   Merry Wanderer, Plaque

HUM 93   Little Fiddler, Plaque

Trumpet Boy
HUM 97 . . . . . . 4½" to 4¾"

①②③④⑤⑥

Many size variations. There are a few rare pieces with the inscription "Design Patent No. 116,404" stamped on the bottom.

HUM 94   Surprise

HUM 96   Little Shopper

HUM 95   Brother

HUM 97   Trumpet Boy

Sister
HUM 98/2/0 . . 4½″ to 4¾″
98/0 . . . . 5¼″ to 5½″
98. . . . . 5¾″ (CE)
①②③④⑤⑥

Many size variations; otherwise very little change between old and new figurines. Old name: "The Shopper." Some pieces have a 1962 copyright date incised.

Eventide
HUM 99 . . . . . . 4¼″x5″
①②③④⑤⑥

Many size variations. Also sold in white overglaze at one time—extremely rare.

Shrine, Table Lamp
HUM 100 . . . . . 7½″ (CE)
①②

Very few ever produced. Only a few examples known to exist. Extremely rare.

To Market, Table Lamp
HUM 101 . . . . . 7½″ (CE)

Listed as closed edition on factory records 20 April 1937. Redesigned and some produced in early 1960's with "tree trunk" post. Some incised with number II/101 and others with 101 only. See HUM 223 for photograph of the redesigned piece.

Volunteers, Table Lamp
HUM 102 (CE)

Listed as closed edition on factory records, 20 April 1937. No known examples.

Farewell, Table Lamp
HUM 103 (CE)

Listed as closed edition on factory records, 20 April 1937. No known examples.

Wayside Devotion, Table Lamp
HUM 104 (CE)

Listed as closed edition on factory records, 3 March 1938. No known examples.

HUM 98   Sister

HUM 99   Eventide

HUM 100   Shrine, Table Lamp

HUM 101   To Market, Table Lamp

HUM 101   rear view

Adoration With Bird
HUM 105 . . . . . 4¾" (CE)

Very limited production. Listed as closed edition on factory records, 24 May 1938. All known examples have "double crown" trademark incised and stamped in blue. Note difference in pigtail of little girl in photograph. This figurine is considered extremely rare.

Merry Wanderer, Plaque with wood frame. (CE)
HUM 106 . . . . . 6"x6"

Extremely rare. Listed as closed edition on factory records, 1 August 1938.

Little Fiddler, Plaque with wood frame. (CE)
HUM 107 . . . . . 6"x6"

Extremely rare. Listed as closed edition on factory records, 1 August 1938.

Angel With Two Children At Feet (CN)
HUM 108

No known examples. Listed on factory records of 14 October 1938 as a wall decoration (wall plaque?).

Happy Traveller
HUM 109 . . . . . 5"
109/0 . . . 4¾" to 5"
109/II . . 7½"
109. . . . . 7¾" (CE)
①②③④⑤⑥

Current production pieces have no size indicator on small size figurines. Listed as "Wanderer" in old catalogues.

Let's Sing
HUM 110/0 . . . 3" to 3¼"
110/I . . . 3½" to 4"
110. . . . . 4" (CE)
①②③④⑤⑥

Many size variations. Some incised numbers are hard to read because of extremely small bases. Some have an incised 1938 copyright date.

(continued)

HUM 105   Adoration With Bird

HUM 106   Merry Wanderer, Plaque with wood frame.

HUM 107 Little Fiddler, Plaque with wood frame

HUM 109 Happy Traveller

Jar style

Bowl style

HUM III /110 Let's Sing, Box

HUM 110 Let's Sing

Let's Sing, Box
   HUM III/110. . 6¼″
                  Bowl Style
                  (CE)
   III/110. . 5¼″
                  Jar Style
   ①②③④⑤⑥

Bowl style first produced in 1938. Jar style first produced and sold in 1964.

Wayside Harmony
   HUM 111 3/0. . 3¾″ to 4″
   111/I . . . 5″ to 5½″
   111. . . . 5½″ (CE)
   ①②③④⑤⑥

Many size variations. Old name: "Just Sittin-Boy." Some models have a 1938 incised copyright date.

Wayside Harmony, Table Lamp
   HUM II/111 . . 7½″ (CE)
   ? ②

This number used briefly in early 1950's. Later changed to 224/I. The only difference is the the boy is slightly larger. Extremely rare.

Just Resting
   HUM 112 3/0. . 3¾″ to 4″
   112/I . . . 4¾″ to 5½″
   112. . . . 5½″ (CE)
   ①②③④⑤⑥

Many size variations. Old name: "Just Sittin-Girl." Some models have a 1938 incised copyright date. There is an unusual example of size 112/I without a basket in front of the girl (not shown).

Just Resting, Table Lamp
   HUM II/112 . . 7½″ (CE)
   ? ②

This number was used briefly in the early 1950's; later changed to 225/l. The only difference is that the girl is slightly larger. Extremely rare.

Heavenly Song, Candle Holder
   HUM 113. . . . . 3½″x4¾″
   ①②③④⑤⑥

Very limited production. Considered rare. Sometimes mistaken for HUM 54 "Silent Night," which is similar.

Let's Sing, Ashtray
   HUM 114. . . . . 3½″x6¼″
   ①②③④⑤⑥

Old model produced with ashtray on left. Considered rare. New model produced with ashtray on right.

HUM 111   Wayside Harmony

HUM 112   Just Resting

HUM 111   Wayside Harmony, Table Lamp
         II/111   224/I

HUM 112   Just Resting, Table Lamp
         II/112   225/I

HUM 113   Heavenly Song, Candle Holder

HUM 114   Let's Sing, Ashtray   Old   New

Advent Candlestick, Girl With Nosegay
   HUM 115 . . . . . 3½″

Advent Candlestick, Girl With Fir Tree
   HUM 116 . . . . . 3½″

Advent Candlestick, Boy With Horse
   HUM 117 . . . . . 3½″
   ①②③④⑤⑥

These three figurines are similar to HUM 239 A, B, & C (without candle holders). Very early models were incised with "Mel" instead of "M. I. Hummel." Reportedly sold only in Germany. Note: "Mel" is the last three letters of "Hum*mel*."

Little Thrifty, Bank
   HUM 118 . . . . . 5″ to 5½″
   ①②③④⑤⑥

This piece is actually a bank. Made with metal lock & key on bottom. Older models have different base design. See photograph.

Postman
   HUM 119 . . . . . 5″ to 5½″
   ①②③④⑤⑥

Many size variations. Has been restyled with new textured finish.

Book Ends: Joyful and Let's Sing (on wooden base)
   HUM 120 . . . . . (CE)

No known examples. Listed as closed edition on factory records, 16 June 1939.

Book Ends: Wayside Harmony and Just Resting (on wooden base)
   HUM 121 . . . . . (CE)

No known examples. Listed as closed edition on factory records, 16 June 1939.

HUM 115   Girl With Nosegay   HUM 116   Girl With Fir Tree
HUM 117   Boy With Horse

HUM 118   Little Thrifty, Bank New   Old

Book Ends: Puppy Love and Serenade With Dog (on wooden base)
   HUM 122 . . . . . (CE)

Factory sample only. Listed as closed edition on factory records, 16 June 1939.

HUM 119　　Postman　　　　"Current"　　　　　　　"Stylized"　　　　　　　"Full Bee"

HUM 122　　Book Ends: Puppy Love and Serenade With Dog (on wooden base)

Max And Moritz
 HUM 123. . . . . 5″ to 5½″
 ①②③④⑤⑥

Much size variation. Most pieces have a 1939 incised copyright date. Has been restyled with new textured finish. Old name: "Good Friends."

Hello
 HUM 124/0 . . . 5¾″ to 6¼″
 124/I . . . 6¾″ to 7″
 124. . . . 6¾″ (CE)
 ①②③④⑤⑥

Many size variations. Earliest models produced had gray coat, gray trousers and pink vest. Changed to brown coat, green trousers and pink vest in early 1950's. Changed to dark brown coat, light brown trousers and blue-white vest in mid-1960's. Old name: "The Boss" or "Der Chef." Size 124/I is currently being produced with modern colors.

Vacation-Time, Plaque
 HUM 125. . . . . 4⅜″x5¼″
 (old style)
 125. . . . . 4″x4¾″
 (new style)
 ①②③④⑤⑥

Restyled in early 1960's. New model has five fence posts while old has six. Old name: "On Holiday" or "Happy Holidays." New models produced without string for hanging, only a hole on back for hanging.

Retreat To Safety, Plaque
 HUM 126. . . . . 4¾″x4¾″
 to 5″x5″
 ①②③④⑤⑥

Older plaques are slightly larger. Slight color variations.

Doctor
 HUM 127. . . . . 4¾″ to 5¼″
 ①②③④⑤⑥

Many size variations. Has been restyled with new textured fin-

(continued)

HUM 123   Max And Moritz

HUM 124   Hello
"Current"   "Full Bee"   "Crown"

HUM 125　　Vacation-Time, Plaque
New　　　　　　　　　　　　　　Old

HUM 127　　Doctor

HUM 126　　Retreat To Safety, Plaque

HUM 128　　Baker

ish. Old name: "The Doll Doctor."

Baker
> **HUM 128 . . . . . 4¾″ to 5″**
> ①②③④⑤⑥

Many size variations. Has been restyled with new textured finish. Slighd color variations.

Band Leader
> **HUM 129 . . . . . 5″ to 5⅞″**
> ①②③④⑤⑥

Many size and color variations. Old name: "Leader."

Duet
> **HUM 130 . . . . . 5″ to 5½″**
> ①②③④⑤⑥

Many size variations. Early crown mark pieces have incised music notes, as well as being painted. Old name: "The Songsters."

Street Singer
> **HUM 131 . . . . . 5″ to 5½″**
> ①②③④⑤⑥

Many size variations. Some slight color variations. Old name: "Soloist."

Star Gazer
> **HUM 132 . . . . . 4¾″**
> ①②③④⑤⑥

Older models have blue shirt. Newer models have purple shirt. Also some color variations on telescope.

Mother's Helper
> **HUM 133 . . . . . 4¾″ to 5″**
> ①②③④⑤⑥

Older pieces slightly larger. Only figurine (in current production) produced with a cat.

HUM 129   Band Leader

HUM 130   Duet

HUM 132   Star Gazer

HUM 131   Street Singer

HUM 133   Mother's Helper

Quartet, Plaque
     HUM 134 . . . . . 5½″x6¼″
     ❶❷❸❹❺❻

Older models have "M. I. Hummel" signature on back. Newer models have signature on front. Older models provided with holes for cord to hang on wall. Newer models have one hole on back for hanging.

Soloist
     HUM 135 . . . . . 4½″x5″
     ❶❷❸❹❺❻

Many size variations between old and new pieces. Old name: "High Tenor."

Friends
     HUM 136/I . . . 5″
     136/V
     (136/5) . . 10¾″ to 11″
     136 . . . . 10½″ (CE)
     ❶❷❸❹❺❻

Sold at one time in reddish brown terra cotta finish in size 136. (10½″) with incised crown trademark. Extremely rare. Old name: "Good Friends" or "Friendship." The small size usually has an incised 1947 copyright date.

Child In Bed, Wall Plaque
     HUM 137 . . . . . 2¾″x2¾″
     (Child looking right)
     137 A . . . 2¾″x2¾″
     (Child looking left)
     (CE)
     137 B . . . 2¾″x2¾″
     (Child looking right)
     (CE)
     ❶❷❸❹❺❻

Also called "Baby Ring with Ladybug" or "Ladybug Plaque." No known examples of 137 A. Current production number 137 only. "M. I. Hummel" signature on back.

HUM 134   Quartet, Plaque

Tiny Baby In Crib, Wall Plaque
     HUM 138 . . . . . 2¼″x3″
                    (CN)

Factory sample only. Never produced for sale.

Flitting Butterfly, Wall Plaque
     HUM 139 . . . . . 2½″x2½″
     ❶❷❸❹❺❻

Early crown mark piece has no dots on girl's dress. "M. I. Hummel" signature on back during all time periods. Redesigned in 1960's with no air space behind girl's head. Also known as "Butterfly Plaque."

HUM 135   Soloist

HUM 136   Friends (terra cotta)

HUM 136   Friends

HUM 137   Child In Bed, Wall Plaque

HUM 138   Tiny Baby In Crib, Wall Plaque

HUM 139   Flitting Butterfly, Wall Plaque

The mail is here, Plaque
  HUM 140..... 4¼″x6¾″
  ①②③④⑤⑥

Also produced and sold in white overglaze at one time. Extremely rare. Old name: "Post Carriage." Also known as "Mail Coach" plaque.

Apple Tree Girl
  HUM 141 3/0.. 4″ to 4¼″
  141/I
  (141) ... 6″ to 6¾″
  141/V... 10¼″
  141/X... 32″
  ①②③④⑤⑥

Has been restyled several times. Early models had tapered brown base. Smaller models made without bird in tree. Many size variations in older pieces. Size 141/V first produced in early 1970's and found in 4, 5 and 6 trademark periods. Size 141/X first produced in 1975. Old name: "Spring" or "Springtime."

Apple Tree Boy
  HUM 142 3/0.. 4″ to 4¼″
  142/I
  (142) ... 6″ to 6⅞″
  142/V... 10¼″
  142/X... 30″
  ①②③④⑤⑥

Has been restyled several times. Early models had tapered brown base. Many size variations in older pieces. Size 142/V first produced in early 1970's and found in 4, 5 and 6 trademark periods only. Size 142/X first produced in mid-1960's with number 142/10 incised and the "stylized" mark is incised rather than stamped.

Old name: "Autumn" or "Fall." Smaller models made without bird in tree.

HUM 140   The mail is here, Plaque

HUM 141   Apple Tree Girl
      141/V   141/I Old   141/I New   141 3/0 New   141 3/0 Old

HUM 142   Apple Tree Boy
      142/V   142/I Old   142/I New   142 3/0 New   142 3/0 Old

Boots
> **HUM 143/0 . . . 5″ to 5½″**
> **143/I . . . 6½″ to 6¾″**
> **143 . . . . . 6¾″ (CE)**
> ①②③④⑤⑥

Many size variations. Old name: "Shoemaker."

Angelic Song
> **HUM 144 . . . . . 4″**
> ①②③④⑤⑥

Little variation between old and new models. Old names: "Angels" or "Holy Communion."

Little Guardian
> **HUM 145 . . . . . 3¾″ to 4″**
> ①②③④⑤⑥

Older models slightly larger.

Holy Water Font, Angel Duet
> **HUM 146 . . . . . 3¼″x4¾″**
> ①②③④⑤⑥

Slight size variation. Variation in wings of angels and construction of back of font.

Holy Water Font, Angel Shrine
> **HUM 147 . . . . . 3″x5″ to**
> **3⅛″x5½″**
> ①②③④⑤⑥

Older models are larger. Old name: "Angel Devotion." Some variation in construction of back of font and water bowl.

> **HUM 148 . . . . . (CN)**

Factory records indicate this was the same as the boy from HUM 60/A (Farm Boy, Book End). Listed as Closed Number on 28 February 1941.

> **HUM 149 . . . . . (CN)**

Factory records indicate this was the same as the girl from HUM 60/B (Goose Girl, Book End). Listed as Closed Number on 28 February 1941.

HUM 143   Boots

Happy Days
> **HUM 150 2/0 . . 4¼″**
> **150/0 . . . 5″ to 5¼″**
> **150/I . . . 6¼″ to 6½″**
> **150 . . . . . 6¼″ (CE)**
> ①②③④⑤⑥

Size 150/0 and 150/I are once again back in current production.

HUM 144   Angelic Song

HUM 145   Little Guardian

HUM 147   Angel Shrine, Holy Water Font

HUM 146   Angel Duet, Holy Water Font

HUM 150   Happy Days

Madonna Holding Child
HUM 151 . . . . . 12½″
① ② ③ ④ ⑤ ⑥

Known as "Madonna with the Blue Cloak." Produced in five color variations—white overglaze (OE)—pastel blue cloak (OE)—dark blue cloak (CE)—brown cloak (CE)—ivory finish (CE). All of the closed editions are considered extremely rare. The figurine had not been produced for many years but has recently been put into current production in white overglaze and pastel blue bearing the 5 and 6 trademarks.

Umbrella Boy
HUM 152/0 A . . 4¾″
152 A
(152 A/II) 8″
① ② ③ ④ ⑤ ⑥

Small size usually found in trademarks 3, 4, 5 and 6 only. Large size has been restyled with a thin umbrella and new textured finish. Crown mark umbrella boy would be considered extremely rare. Old name: "In Safety" or "Boy Under Umbrella." The copyright date on the small size is 1957. Large size first produced in 1942; small size first produced in 1954.

Umbrella Girl
HUM 152/0 B . . 4¾″
152 B (152
B/II) . . . . 8″
① ② ③ ④ ⑤ ⑥

Small size usually found in trademarks 3, 4, 5 and 6 only. Large size has been restyled with a thin umbrella and new textured finish. Crown mark umbrella girl would be considered extremely rare. Old name: "In Safety" or "Girl Under Umbrella." Copyright date of 1951 incised on large size and 1957 incised on small size.
(continued)

HUM 151   Madonna Holding Child

HUM 151 three color variations

118

HUM 152   Umbrella Boy

HUM 152   Umbrella Girl

HUM 153   Auf Wiedersehen

Boy with hat **(CE)**

Large size first produced in 1949; small size first produced in 1954.

Auf Wiedersehen
HUM 153/0 . . . 5½" to 6"
153/0 (boy with
hat) . . . . 5¼" (CE)
153/I . . . 6¾" to 7"
153 . . . . . 7" (CE)

①②③④⑤⑥

Boy wearing hat produced in small size only. Usually with full bee trademark and "0" size designator directly under the number "153"—considered rare. Both sizes have been restyled. Also called "Good Bye" in old catalogues.

Waiter
HUM 154/0 . . . 6" to 6¼"
154/I . . . 6½" to 7"
154 . . . . . 6½" (CE)

①②③④⑤⑥

Many size variations. Older models have gray coat and gray trousers. Newer models have blue coat and brown trousers. Has been produced with various names on bottle. "Rhein-wine" most common. "Whisky," "Hiher Mchie" and other illegible names have been used. Old name: "Chef of Service."

HUM 155 . . . . . (CN)
Factory records indicate: Madonna with cloak, sitting with child on her lap. Listed as Closed Number on 18 May 1943.

HUM 156 . . . . . (CN)
Factory records indicate: Wall picture with sitting woman and child. Listed as Closed Number on 18 May 1943.

HUM 157 . . . . . (CN)
Factory records indicate: Boy standing with flower basket. Listed as Closed Number on 17 September 1943.

HUM 154 **Waiter**
154/0   154/I   154. **(CE)**

HUM 163 **Whitsuntide**   New   Old

120

HUM 164   Holy Water Font, Worship

HUM 165   Swaying Lullaby, Wall Plaque

HUM 158 . . . . . (CN)

Factory records indicate: Girl standing with dog in her arms. Listed as Closed Number on 17 September 1943.

HUM 159 . . . . . (CN)

Factory records indicate: Girl standing with flowers in her arms. Listed as Closed Number on 17 September 1943.

HUM 160 . . . . . (CN)

Factory records indicate: Girl standing in tiered dress and bouquet of flowers. Listed as Closed Number on 17 September 1943.

HUM 161 . . . . . (CN)

Factory records indicate: Girl standing with hands in her pockets. Listed as Closed Number on 17 September 1943.

HUM 162 . . . . . (CN)

Factory records indicate: Girl standing with pocket-book (handbag). Listed as Closed Number on 11 October 1943.

Whitsuntide
HUM 163 . . . . . 6½″ to 7″
① ② ③ ? ⑤ ⑥

Older models are larger than newer models. Old name: "Christmas." Sometimes called "Happy New Year." Angel on base holds red or yellow candle on older models. Unusual variation has small hole in angel's cupped hands where candle should be. Has been considered rare but is again in current production with 5 and 6 trademarks.

Holy Water Font, Worship
HUM 164 . . . . . 3¼″x5″
① ② ③ ④ ⑤ ⑥

Older models do not have rim on back side of bowl. Also color variation on lip of water bowl.

Swaying Lullaby, Wall Plaque
HUM 165 . . . . . 4½″x5¼″
① ② ③ ? ⑤ ⑥

Older models have "M. I. Hummel" signature on back. Newer models have signature on front lower right corner. Old name: "Child in a Hammock." Inscription reads: "Dreaming of better times." Has been considered rare but is again in current production with 5 and 6 trademarks.

Boy With Bird, Ashtray
   HUM 166. . . . . 3¼″x6″
   ①②③④⑤⑥

Holy Water Font, Angel-Bird
   HUM 167. . . . . 3¼″x4⅛″
   ①②③④⑤⑥

Newer models have a hole at top of font for hanging. Older models have hole on back of font for hanging. Variations in color on lip of water bowl.

Standing Boy, Wall Plaque
   HUM 168. . . . . 4⅛″x5½″
   ①②③ ? ⑤⑥

Has been considered rare but is again in current production with 5 and 6 trademarks. Older models have "Hummel" signature on front, lower left. New models have "M. I. Hummel" signature incised on back.

Bird Duet
   HUM 169. . . . . 3¾″ to 4″
   ①②③④⑤⑥

Many variations between old and new figurines. Restyled in 1960's. Variations in angel's wings, gown and position of baton. Color variations in birds, angel's hair and gown, as well as music stand.

HUM 166   Boy With Bird, Ashtray

HUM 167   Holy Water Font, Angel-Bird

HUM 168   Standing Boy, Wall Plaque Old

HUM 169   Bird Duet   Old   New

School Boys
> **HUM 170/I ... 7¼″ to 7½″**
> **170/III.. 10″ to**
> **10¼″**
> **170..... 10″ (CE)**
> ①②③④⑤⑥

Old name: "Difficult Problems." Some color variation on older models. Small size first produced in early 1960's. Has 1961 copyright date incised. Large size has been restyled with new textured finish in 1970's. Has 1972 incised copyright date.

Little Sweeper
> **HUM 171..... 4¼″**
> ①②③④⑤⑥

Very little change between old and new models. Old name: "Mother's Helper."

Festival Harmony
(Mandolin)
> **HUM 172/0 ... 8″**
> **172/II .. 10¼″ to**
> **10¾″**
> **172..... 10¾″ (CE)**
> ①②③④⑤⑥

Three variations. Old crown mark piece has bird resting on flowers in front of angel (rare). Restyled in 1950's with bird resting on mandolin and one flower on angel's gown. Restyled in late 1960's with new textured finish and flowers placed at angel's feet. Variations in color of gown and color of birds. Small size produced since mid 1960's in one style only.

HUM 170   School Boys

HUM 171   Little Sweeper

HUM 172   Festival Harmony (Mandolin)
    "Crown"   "Full Bee"   "Stylized"

Festival Harmony (Flute)
   HUM 173/0 . . . 8″
         173/II . . 10¼″ to 11″
         173 . . . . . 11″ (CE)
         ①②③④⑤⑥

Three variations. Old crown mark piece has much larger bird and flowers in front of angel (rare). Restyled in 1950's with smaller bird and one flower on angel's gown. Restyled in late 1960's with new textured finish and flowers placed at angel's feet. Variations in color of gown and color of birds. Small size produced since mid-1960's in one style only.

She Loves Me, She Loves Me Not!
   HUM 174 . . . . . 4¼″
         ①②③④⑤⑥

Has been restyled several times. Early crown mark piece has smaller feather in boy's hat, no flower on left fence post and eyes open. The 2, 3 & 4 trademark period pieces have a flower on left fence post and eyes open. Current production pieces have no flower on left fence post (same as crown mark piece) but with eyes closed.

Mother's Darling
   HUM 175 . . . . . 5½″
         ①②③④⑤⑥

Older models have pink and green colored kerchiefs (bags). Newer models have blue ones. Older models do not have polka dots on head scarf. Old name: Happy Harriet."

Happy Birthday
   HUM 176/0 . . . 5″ to 5¼″
         176/I . . . 5¾″ to 6″
         176 . . . . . 5½″ (CE)

Small size has oval base. Large size has round base.

HUM 173   Festival Harmony (Flute)
   "Crown"   "Full Bee"   "Stylized"

HUM 174   She Loves Me, She Loves Me Not!

"Current"   "Crown"

HUM 175   Mother's Darling   Newer model

HUM 176   Happy Birthday   176/0

School Girls
> **HUM 177/I ... 7½″**
> **177/III .. 9½″**
> **177 ..... 9½″ (CE)**
> ①②③④⑤⑥

Old name: "Master Piece." Some color variations on older models. Only the small size has 1961 incised as the copyright date. Large size restyled with new textured finish in 1970's. It has 1972 incised as the copyright date. See HUM 255 (Stitch in Time) and HUM 256 (Knitting Lesson).

Photographer
> **HUM 178 ..... 4¾″ to 5¼″**
> ①②③④⑤⑥

Many size variations. Older models are larger. Newer models have 1948 incised as the copyright date. Some color variations on dog and camera. Has been restyled.

Coquettes
> **HUM 179 ..... 5″ to 5¼″**
> ①②③④⑤⑥

Older pieces slightly larger. Some color variations. Has been restyled.

Tuneful Good Night, Wall Plaque
> **HUM 180 ..... 5″x4¾″**
> ①②③④⑤⑥

Old name: "Happy Bugler." Has been considered rare but is again in current production with 5 and 6 trademarks.

Old Man Reading Newspaper
> **HUM 181 ..... 6¾″ (CN)**

This piece was made as a sample only and was not approved by the Siessen Convent for production. It was not considered typical of her work. It is an exact reproduction of one of Sister M. I. Hummel's early sketches. It was listed as a closed number on 18 February 1948.

HUM 177 School Girls

HUM 178   Photographer

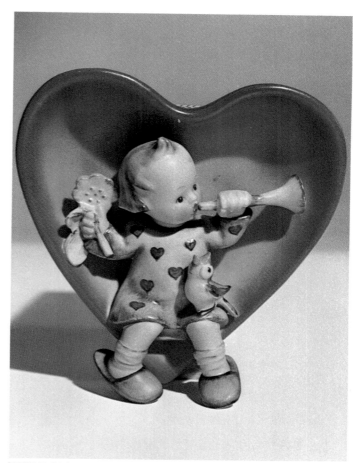

HUM 180   Tuneful Good Night, Wall Plaque

HUM 179   Coquettes

HUM 181   Old Man Reading Newspaper

Good Friends
HUM 182 . . . . . 4″ to 4¼″
① ② ③ ④ ⑤ ⑥

Restyled by Gerhard Skrobek in 1976. Current model slightly larger. Called "Friends" in old catalogues.

Forest Shrine
HUM 183 . . . . . 9″
① ② ③ ④ ⑤ ⑥

Older models' deer have shiny finish, newer models have a dull finish. Has been considered rare but is again in production with 5 and 6 trademarks. Old name: "Doe at Shrine."

Latest News
HUM 184 . . . . . 5″ to 5¼″
① ② ③ ④ ⑤ ⑥

Older models were made with square base and boy's eyes open. Restyled in mid 1960's and changed to round base and boy's eyes looking down at paper. At one time the newspaper was produced without any name. Visitors to the factory could have the name of their choice put on. An endless variety of names can be found. Most common names are: "Das Allerneueste," "Latest News," and "Münchener Presse." Some catalogues list as 184/O.S. which means: Ohne Schrift (Without lettering).

Accordion Boy
HUM 185 . . . . . 5″ to 6″
① ② ③ ④ ⑤ ⑥

Many size variations. Larger pieces made during the 1950's with full bee trademark. Slight color variations on the accordion. Old name: "On the Alpine Pasture."

Sweet Music
HUM 186 . . . . . 5″ to 5½″
① ② ③ ④ ⑤ ⑥

Many size variations. On old crown mark pieces boy has striped slippers. Old name: "Playing To The Dance."

HUM 182   Good Friends
New style   Old style

HUM 183   Forest Shrine

HUM 184   Latest News   New style   Old style

HUM 186   Sweet Music
New   Old

HUM 185   Accordion Boy
New   Old

M. I. Hummel Plaques
(in English)
HUM 187 . . . . . 4″x5½″
①②③④⑤⑥

There seems to have been an endless variety of plaques produced through the years, some for dealers and some for collectors. At one time in recent years dealers names were printed on the plaques for Australian dealers only. Current display plaques for collectors are incised 187 A. Two copyright dates have been used, 1947 and 1976.

This photo pictures only a small portion of the many variations issued.

Celestial Musician
    HUM 188 . . . . . 7″
        ❶❷❸❹❺❻

Older models are slightly larger. Some models have 1948 copyright date. Also sold in white overglaze at one time—extremely rare.

Old Woman Knitting
    HUM 189 . . . . . 6¾″ (CN)

Old Woman Walking To Market
    HUM 190 . . . . . 6¾″ (CN)

Old Man Walking To Market
    HUM 191 . . . . . 6¾″ (CN)

HUM 189 through HUM 191 were made as samples only and were not approved by the Siessen Convent for production. They were not considered typical of her work but are exact reproductions of some of Sister M.I. Hummel's early sketches. They were listed as closed numbers on 14 May 1948.

HUM 188　Celestial Musician

HUM 189 Old Woman Knitting

HUM 191 Old Man Walking To Market

HUM 190 Old Woman Walking To Market

Candlelight, Candle Holder
   HUM 192 . . . . . 6¾″ to 7″
   ①②③④⑤⑥

Older models were produced with a long red ceramic candle. Newer models have a short candle holder ending in angels' hands. Both models have receptical for holding a wax candle. Older models are slightly larger. Old name: "Carrier of Light." The incised copyright date on both models is 1948. Short candle style produced after 1960.

Angel Duet, Candle Holder
   HUM 193 . . . . . 5″
   ①②③④⑤⑥

Produced without holder for candle as HUM 261. Some models have a 1948 incised copyright date. See comparison of back view on page 166. Also sold in white overglaze at one time—extremely rare.

Watchful Angel
   HUM 194 . . . . . 6¼″ to 6¾″
   ①②③④⑤⑥

Older models are usually larger. Most models have 1948 incised copyright date. Old name: "Angelic Care."

Barnyard Hero
   HUM 195 2/0 . . 3¾″ to 4″
   195/I . . . 5½″
   195.   . . . 5¾″ to 6″
                (CE)
   ①②③④⑤⑥

Many size variations. Both sizes have been restyled in recent years. Variation in boy's hands in small size only: old model has one hand on each side of fence; new model, one hand on top of the other one. Most models have a 1948 incised copyright date.

HUM 192   Candlelight, Candle Holder
   New style   Old style

HUM 193   Angel Duet, Candle Holder

HUM 194   Watchful Angel

HUM 195/I   Barnyard Hero

Telling Her Secret

    HUM 196/0 . . . 5″ to 5½″
           196/I . . . 6½″ to 6¾″
           196. . . . 6¾″ (CE)

①②③④⑤⑥

Slightly restyled in recent years. Old name: "The Secret." Girl on the right same as HUM 258 (Which Hand?).

Be Patient

    HUM 197 2/0 . . 4¼″ to 4½″
           197/I . . . 6″ to 6¼″
           197. . . . 6¼″ (CE)

①②③④⑤⑥

Newer models have 1948 incised copyright date. Old name: "Mother of Ducks."

Home From Market

    HUM 198 2/0 . . 4½″ to 4¾″
           198/I . . . 5½″
           198. . . . 5¾″ to 6″
               (CE)

①②③④⑤⑥

Many size variations. Older models are larger than new. Newer models have a 1948 incised copyright date.

Feeding Time

    HUM 199/0 . . . 4¼″ to 4½″
           199/I . . . 5½″ to 5¾″
           199. . . . 5¾″ (CE)

①②③④⑤⑥

Many size variations. The girl is blonde on older figurines. Restyled in mid-1960's with new features and dark hair. Newer models have a 1948 incised copyright date.

HUM 196   Telling Her Secret

HUM 197   Be Patient

HUM 198   Home From Market

HUM 199   Feeding Time   Old style   New style

Little Goat Herder

> **HUM 200/0 . . . 4½″ to 4¾″**
> **200/I . . . 5″ to 5½″**
> **200 . . . . . 5½″ to 5¾″**
> **(CE)**

①②③④⑤⑥

Older models have a blade of grass between the hind legs of the small goat. Newer models do not. Newer models have a 1948 incised copyright date. Old name: "Goat Boy."

Retreat To Safety

> **HUM 201 2/0. . 3¾″ to 4″**
> **201/I . . . 5½″ to 5¾″**
> **201 . . . . . 5¾″ to 6″**
> **(CE)**

①②③④⑤⑥

Many size variations. Both sizes have been restyled in recent years. Variation in boy's hands in small size only: old models had one hand on each side of fence, new model one hand on top of other one. Most models have a 1948 incised copyright date. Old name: "Afraid."

Old Man Reading Newspaper, Table Lamp

> **HUM 202 . . . . . 8½″ (CN)**

This piece was made as a sample only and was not approved by the Siessen Convent for production. It was not considered a typical piece. Same figure as HUM 181 on lamp base. Listed as closed number on 18 August 1948.

Signs Of Spring

> **HUM 203 2/0. . 4″**
> **203/I . . . 5″ to 5½″**
> **203 . . . . . 5¼″ (CE)**

①②③④⑤⑥

Many size variations. At one time, only the small size was made with the girl wearing both shoes. Full Bee trademark pieces found both ways. Newer models have a 1948 incised copyright date. Old name: "Scandal." "Two shoe" variety considered rare.

HUM 200   Little Goat Herder   200/I (New style)

HUM 201   Retreat To Safety   201/I

**HUM 202   Old Man Reading Newspaper,
Table Lamp**

HUM 203   Signs Of Spring   203 2/0 (Old style)

203 2/0 (New style)

Weary Wanderer

HUM 204. . . . . 5½″ to 6″

①②③④⑤⑥

Many size variations. Most models have 1949 as the incised copyright date. Old name: "Tired Little Traveler." Has been restyled with new textured finish. The word "Lauterbach" on the back of figurine is the name of a village used in an old German song.

M. I. Hummel Store Plaque (German) (CE)

HUM 205. . . . . 5½″ to 4¼″

①②

Three color variations of lettering: All black lettering, black and red combination as pictured, and all black except the beginning letters 'O,' 'H,' and 'F' in red lettering. Listed as closed edition on 18 June 1949.

Holy Water Font, Angel Cloud

HUM 206. . . . . 3¼″x4¾″

①②③④⑤⑥

At least three different variations. Older models do not have rim on back side of bowl. Also color variation on lip of water bowl. Has been considered rare but is again in current production with 5 and 6 trademarks. Newer models have a 1949 incised copyright date.

Holy Water Font, Heavenly Angel

HUM 207. . . . . 3″x5″

①②③④⑤⑥

Older models have hole for hanging on back. Newer models have hole on front. Newer models have a 1949 incised copyright date.

HUM 204   Weary Wanderer

HUM 205   M. I. Hummel Store Plaque (German)

HUM 206   Holy Water Font, Angel Cloud

HUM 207   Holy Water Font, Heavenly Angel

**M. I. Hummel Store Plaque
(in French) (CE)**

HUM 208.....5½″x4″

Two known variations. Made
with dotted "i" and without
quotation marks on Hummel.
Newer model has quotation
marks: "HUMMEL" + "Reg.
trade mark."

**M. I. Hummel Store Plaque
(in Swedish) (CE)**

HUM 209.....5½″x4″

Extremely rare.

**M. I. Hummel Store Plaque
(Schmid Bros.) (CE)**

HUM 210.....5½″x4″

Normal store plaque with
"SCHMID BROS. INC. BOS-
TON" embossed on side of sat-
chel of Merry Wanderer. Extremely rare.

**M. I. Hummel Store Plaque
(in English) (CE)**

HUM 211.....5½″x4″

All the lettering on this plaque
is in lower case letters. The
word "Oeslau" is used as the
location of W. Goebel Porzellanfabrik. Extremely rare.

**"Orchestra" (CN)
HUM 212**

Most notes from factory state:
"No information available" on
this number. However, one old
list indicates: "orchestra A–F"
and the date "13 May 51." This
is possibly a number assigned to
a Hummel orchestra as a set,
such as Nativity Set HUM 214.

**M. I. Hummel Store Plaque
(in Spanish) (CE)**

HUM 213.....5¾″x4¼″

Extremely rare.

HUM 208   M. I. Hummel Store Plaque (in French)

HUM 209   M. I. Hummel Store Plaque (in Swedish)

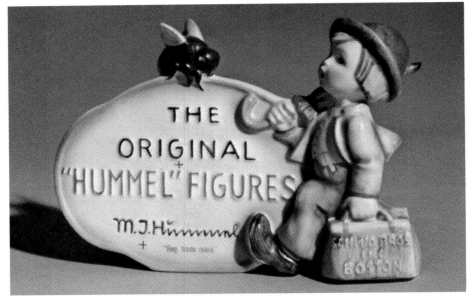

HUM 210   M. I. Hummel Store Plaque (Schmid Bros.)

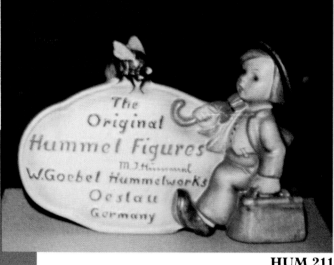

HUM 211

unpainted factory sample

HUM 211   M. I. Hummel Store Plaque (in English)

HUM 213   M. I. Hummel Store Plaque (in Spanish)

Nativity Set With Wooden Stable

HUM 214

214 A   Virgin Mary and
      Infant Jesus (one
      piece . . . . . . 6½″ (CE)

214/A   Virgin Mary 6¼″
                to 6½″

214/A   Infant Jesus 1½″x3½″

214/B   Joseph . . . . . 7½″

214/C   Angel, standing
       "Good Night".3½″

214/D   Angel, kneeling
       "Angel Serenade".3″

214/E   We Congratulate . . 3¾″

214/F   Shepherd, standing
       with sheep. . 7″

214/G   Shepherd, kneeling.5″

214/H   Shepherd Boy,
       kneeling with flute
       "Little Tooter" . . 3¾″
                to 4″

214/J   Donkey . . . . 5″

214/K   Ox (cow) . . . 3½″x6¼″

214/L   Moorish King,
       standing . . . 8″ to 8¼″

214/M   King, kneeling on
       one knee . . . 5½″

214/N   King, kneeling, with
       cash-box . . . 5½″

214/O   Lamb . . . . . . 1¾″x2½″

②③④⑤⑥

First produced and sold in 1952. A complete set was once produced and sold in white overglaze finish. No longer sold in this finish. Early production of HUM 214 A (Virgin Mary and Infant Jesus) was as one unit. Because of production problems, it was later produced as two units, both with the same number (214/A) incised on base of each piece. The one-piece unit is considered rare. Some Nativity set pieces have a 1951 incised copyright date. HUM 214/C, 214/D, 214/E and 214/H are not always included in sets and are considered as "extra" pieces. Considered rare in white overglaze finish.

HUM 214   **Nativity Set With Wooden Stable**

146

HUM 214   rare white pieces

HUM 214 A   Old style, New style

HUM 215 . . . . . (CN)

Factory records indicate a child Jesus, standing with lamb in arms. Listed as Closed Number on 16 August 1951. No known example.

HUM 216 . . . . . (CN)

Factory records indicate Joyful, ashtray without rest for cigarette. Listed as Closed Number on 10 September 1951. No known example.

Boy With Toothache
HUM 217 . . . . . 5¼″ to 5½″
②③④⑤⑥

Older pieces are slightly larger. "©WG" appears after the "M. I. Hummel" signature on some pieces. Old name: "At The Dentist" or "Toothache." Newer models have a 1951 incised copyright date.

Birthday Serenade
HUM 218 2/0 . . 4¼″ to 4½″
218/0
(218) . . . 5¼″
②③④⑤⑥

Early models bearing a 1952 incised copyright date have boy playing horn, girl playing accordion. Newer models bearing a 1965 incised copyright date have boy playing accordion, girl playing horn. This change was made at the request of the convent. The large size (HUM 218/0) has been considered rare but is again back in current production with current trademark with boy playing accordion and girl playing horn with a 1952 incised copyright date. This is an error. It should be 1965. Note that a tie has been added to the boy when he plays the accordion.

(continued)

HUM 217 Boy With Toothache

HUM 218 **Birthday Serenade**   New style   Old style

HUM 219 **Little Velma**

HUM 220 **We Congratulate (with base)**

Little Velma
HUM 219/2/0 . 4″ (CN)

According to factory records this figurine was produced in very limited numbers, (possibly as few as 12 pieces). The name "Little Velma" was affectionately assigned to this piece in honor of the lady that first brought it to the attention of, and sold it to, this author.

We Congratulate (with base)
HUM 220 . . . . . 3¾″ to 4″
220 2/0 . . 4″ (CE)

②③④⑤⑥

Early production pieces carry the incised number 220 2/0. Later production dropped the 2/0 size designator and added 1952 incised copyright date. This figurine is the same as HUM 214/E (part of Nativity set) except with base and no flowers in girl's hair. Also note lederhosen straps added to boy.

Happy Pastime—Candy jar
HUM 221 . . . . (CN)

This piece was made as a sample only and was never produced for sale.

Madonna Plaque (with metal frame)
HUM 222 . . . . 4″x5″ (CE)

②③

Some variation in the metal frames. Found without frame with full bee trademark but unconfirmed if actually sold that way. Similar in design to HUM 48.

To Market, Table Lamp
HUM 223 . . . . 9½″

②③④⑤⑥

Similar to HUM 101 or II/101 table lamp with the exception of a flower on branch of tree trunk. Measures 5¼″ across base. Called "Surprise" in 1955 catalogue.

HUM 221   Happy Pastime—Candy jar

HUM 222   Madonna Plaque (with metal frame)

HUM 223   To Market, Table Lamp   HUM II/101

Wayside Harmony, Table Lamp

> **HUM 224/I . . 7½″**
> **224/II . 9½″**
> **224 . . . . 9½″ (CE)**
> ②③④⑤⑥

Large size same as small with the exception of a flower on branch of tree trunk. Small size measures 4¼″ across base. Large size measures 6¼″ across base.

Just Resting, Table Lamp

> **HUM 225/I . . 7½″**
> **225/II . 9½″**
> **225 . . . . 9½″ (CE)**
> ②③④⑤⑥

Large size same as small with the exception of a flower on branch of tree trunk. Small size measures 4¼″ across base. Large size measures 6¼″ across base.

HUM 224/I   Wayside Harmony, Table Lamp
HUM 225/I   Just Resting, Table Lamp

HUM 226   The mail is here

The mail is here
   HUM 226.... 4¼″x6″
   ②③④⑤⑥
Older pieces are slightly larger. Also called "Mail Coach". Usually has 1952 as the incised copyright date.

She Loves Me, She Loves Me Not, Table Lamp
   HUM 227.... 7½″
   ②③④⑤⑥
Measures 4″ across base. Boy has eyes open.

Good Friends, Table Lamp
   HUM 228.... 7½″
   ②③④⑤⑥
Measures 4¼″ across base.

Apple Tree Girl, Table Lamp
   HUM 229.... 7½″
   ②③④⑤⑥
Measures 4¼″ across base. Old name: "Spring" or "Springtime".

HUM 228   Good Friends, Table Lamp
HUM 227   She Loves Me, She Loves Me Not, Table Lamp

152

HUM 229   Apple Tree Girl, Table Lamp   **HUM 230   Boy**

HUM 231   Birthday Serenade, Table Lamp

HUM 234   Birthday Serenade

Apple Tree Boy, Table Lamp
HUM 230.... 7½″
②③④⑤⑥

Measures 4¼″ across base. Old names: "Autumn" or "Fall" table lamp.

Birthday Serenade, Table Lamp
HUM 231.... 9¾″
② ? ?⑤⑥

Measures 6″ across base. Has hole for electrical switch on top of base. Has been considered rare but is again in production with 5 and 6 trademarks. Has 1954 as the incised copyright date on early models. On current production pieces the musical instruments are reversed.

Happy Days, Table Lamp
HUM 232.... 9¾″
② ? ?⑤⑥

Measures 6″ across base. Has hole for electrical switch on top of base. Has been considered rare but is again in production with 5 and 6 trademarks. Has 1954 as the incised copyright date on early models.

HUM 233.... (CN)

Factory records indicate a sample of a boy feeding birds. Listed as Closed Number on 7 September 1954. No known examples. Gerhard Skrobek, current Master Modeller at the factory, stated that this was the first figure he sculptured after starting to work for W. Goebel Porzellanfabrik in 1954. It was later restyled and now appears as HUM 300.

Birthday Serenade, Table Lamp
HUM 234.... 7¾″
②③④⑤⑥

Similar to HUM 231 with the exception of having no flower on branch of tree trunk. Has 1954 as the incised copyright date. On current production pieces the musical instruments are reversed.

153

Happy Days, Table Lamp
HUM 235.... 7¾"
② ③ ④ ⑤ ⑥

Similar to HUM 232 with the exception of having no flower on branch of tree trunk. Has 1954 as the incised copyright date.

HUM 236.... (ON)

Factory records contain no information at all regarding this number. It has therefore been listed as an Open Number and may be assigned to a future item.

Star Gazer, Wall Plaque
HUM 237..... 4¾" x 5"
(CN)

This piece was made as a sample only and not produced for sale as an open edition. It was once seen in white overglaze at the factory in Germany but could not be located later for a picture.

Angel with Lute
HUM 238 A.. 2" to 2½"
④ ⑤ ⑥

Similar to HUM 38 except without holder for candle. Has a 1967 incised copyright date. Known as part of "Angel Trio".

Angel With Accordion
HUM 238 B.. 2" to 2½"
④ ⑤ ⑥

Similar to HUM 39 except without holder for candle. Has a 1967 incised copyright date. Known as part of "Angel Trio".

Angel With Trumpet
HUM 238 C.. 2" to 2½"
④ ⑤ ⑥

Similar to HUM 40 except without holder for candle. Has a 1967 incised copyright date. Known as part of "Angel Trio".

HUM 232   Happy Days, Table Lamp   HUM 235   Happy Days

Girl With Nosegay
HUM 239 A.. 3½"
④ ⑤ ⑥

Similar to HUM 115 except without holder for candle. Has a 1967 incised copyright date. Known as part of "Children Trio".

Girl With Doll
HUM 239 B.. 3½"
④ ⑤ ⑥

Similar to HUM 116 except without holder for candle. Girl holds doll instead of fir tree. Has a 1967 incised copyright date. Known as part of "Children Trio".

Boy With Horse
HUM 239 C.. 3½"
④ ⑤ ⑥

Similar to HUM 117 except without holder for candle. Boy holds horn instead of holder for candle. Has a 1967 incised copyright date. Known as part of "Children Trio".

HUM 238 B/C/A   **Angel With Accordion**   **Angel With Trumpet**   **Angel with Lute**

HUM 239 A/B/C   **Girl With Nosegay**   **Girl With Doll**   **Boy With Horse**

Little Drummer
> **HUM 240 . . . . 4″ to 4¼″**
> ②③④⑤⑥

Slight size variation. Has a 1955 incised copyright date. Sometimes called "Drummer".

Holy Water Font, Angel Joyous News With Lute
> **HUM 241 . . . . (CN)**

This piece was made as a sample only and not produced for sale as an open edition. Listed as a closed number 6 April 1955.

Angel Lights, Candle Holder
> **HUM 241 . . . . 10⅓″x8⅓″**

This number was assigned to this newly designed piece in error. It may be corrected later. Usually sold with round plate with which this piece is designed to fit. Trademarks 5 and 6 only.

Holy Water Font, Angel Joyous News With Trumpet
> **HUM 242 . . . . (CN)**

This piece was made as a sample only and not produced for sale as an open edition. Listed as a closed number 6 April 1955.

Holy Water Font, Madonna And Child
> **HUM 243 . . . . . 3⅛″ x 4″**
> ②③④⑤⑥

Has a 1955 incised copyright date.

HUM 240   Little Drummer

HUM 242   Holy Water Font, Angel Joyous News With Trumpet
HUM 241   With Lute

HUM 241   Angel Lights, Candle Holder

HUM 243   Holy Water Font, Madonna And Child

157

HUM 244.... (ON)

Factory records contain no information at all regarding this number. It has therefore been listed as an Open Number and may be assigned to a future item.

HUM 245.... (ON)

Factory records contain no information at all regarding this number. It has therefore. been listed as an Open Number and may be assigned to a future item.

Holy Water Font, Holy Family

HUM 246.... 3⅛″x4½″
②③④⑤⑥

Has a 1955 incised copyright date.

Standing Madonna With Child

HUM 247.... 13″ (CN)

This piece was made as a sample only and not produced for sale as an open edition.

Holy Water Font, Guardian Angel

Hum 248.... 2¼″x5½″
248/O . 2⅜″x5⅜″
(CE)
248/I . . 2¾″x6¼″
(CE)
?③④⑤⑥

Has a 1959 incised copyright date. Restyled version of HUM 29 because of fragile wings. Now produced in one size only.

Madonna And Child (in relief) Wall Plaque

HUM 249.... 6¾″x8¾″
(CN)

This piece was made as a sample only and not produced for sale as an open edition. Similar to HUM 48/V except without background or frame.

HUM 246   Holy Water Font, Holy Family

HUM 247   Standing Madonna With Child

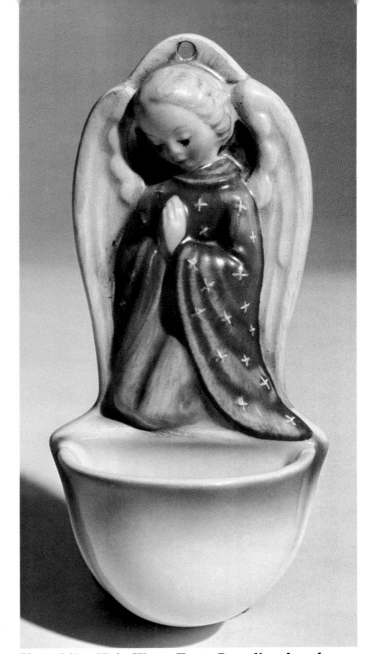

Hum 248   Holy Water Font, Guardian Angel

**HUM 249   Madonna And Child (in relief)
Wall Plaque**

159

Little Goat Herder, Book End
 HUM 250 A . . 5½″
First sold in U. S. in 1964.

Feeding Time, Book End
 HUM 250 B . . 5½″
First sold in U. S. in 1964.

Good Friends, Book End
 HUM 251 A . . 5″
First sold in U. S. in 1964.

She Loves Me, She Loves Me Not!, Book End
 HUM 251 B . . 5″
First sold in U. S. in 1964.

Apple Tree Girl, Book End
 HUM 252 A . . 5″
First sold in U. S. in 1964.

Apple Tree Boy, Book End
 HUM 252 B . . 5″
First sold in U. S. in 1964.

HUM 253 . . . . 4½″ (CN)
Factory records indicate a girl with basket similar to the one in HUM 52 (Going to Grandma's). No known examples.

HUM 254 . . . . 4¼″ (CN)
Factory records indicate a girl playing a mandolin similar to the one in HUM 150 (Happy Days). No known examples.

Stitch In Time
 HUM 255 . . . . 6½″ to 6¾″
 ③④⑤⑥
Has a 1963 incised copyright date. First sold in U. S. in 1964. Similar to one girl used in HUM 256 (Knitting Lesson) and HUM 177 (School Girls).

HUM 250 A Little Goat Herder, Book End
 HUM 250 B Feeding Time, Book End

HUM 251 A Good Friends, Book End
 HUM 251 B She Loves Me, She Loves Me Not!, Book End

HUM 252 A   Apple Tree Girl, Book End   **HUM 252 B   Apple Tree Boy, Book End**

HUM 255   Stitch In Time

Knitting Lesson
HUM 256.... 7½"
③④⑤⑥

Has a 1963 incised copyright date. First sold in U.S. in 1964. Similar to two girls used in HUM 177 (School Girls).

For Mother
HUM 257.... 5" to 5¼"
③④⑤⑥

Has a 1963 incised copyright date. First sold in U. S. in 1964.

Which Hand?
HUM 258.... 5¼" to 5½"
③④⑤⑥

Has a 1963 incised copyright date. First sold in U. S. in 1964. Similar to girl used in HUM 196 (Telling Her Secret).

Girl With Accordion
HUM 259.... 4" (CN)

It depicts a girl playing an accordion as in HUM 218 (Birthday Serenade). This piece was made as a sample only and not produced for sale as an open edition. Listed as Closed Number 8 November 1962.

HUM 256   Knitting Lesson

HUM 257   For Mother

HUM 258   Which Hand?

HUM 259   Girl With Accordion

Large nativity set with wooden stable
   HUM 260....

        260 A .... 9¾″
        Madonna

        260 B .... 11¾″
        Saint Joseph

        260 C .... 5¾″
        Infant Jesus

        260 D .... 5¼″
        Good Night

        260 E .... 4¼″
        Angel Serenade

        260 F .... 6¼″
        We Congratulate

        260 G .... 11¾″
        Shepherd, standing

        260 H .... 3¾″
        **Sheep, standing
with lamb**

        260 J ..... 7″
        **Shepherd Boy,
kneeling**

        260 K .... 5⅛″
        Little Tooter

        260 L .... 7½″
        Donkey, standing

        260 M ... 6 x 11″
        Cow, lying

        260 N .... 12¾″
        **Moorish King,
standing**

        260 O ... 12″
        King, standing

        260 P .... 9″
        King, kneeling

        260 R .... 3¼ x 4″
        One Sheep, lying

Angel Duet
HUM 261.... 5"

④⑤⑥

Same as HUM 193 without holder for candle. Has a 1968 copyright date. Notice position of angel's arm in rear view.

Heavenly Lullaby
HUM 262.... 3½x5"

④⑤⑥

Same as HUM 24/I without hole for candle. Has a 1968 copyright date.

Merry Wanderer, Wall Plaque (in relief)
HUM 263.... 4x5¾" (CN)

This piece is a Merry Wanderer figurine made without base, flattened on the back side with a hole provided for hanging. Samples only. Never mass produced.

HUM 261   Angel Duet   HUM 193

HUM 261   rear view   HUM 193

HUM 262   Heavenly Lullaby

HUM 263   Merry Wanderer, Wall Plaque (in relief)

Annual Plate, 1971 Heavenly Angel

HUM 264.... 7½″ (CE)

1971 was the 100th anniversary of W. Goebel Porzellanfabrik. The annual plate was issued in commemoration of that occasion. Each employee of the company was presented with a 1971 annual plate bearing a special inscription on the back. These plates with the special inscription have become a highly sought after collector's item because of the very limited production. Produced with the 4 trademark only.

Annual Plate, 1972 Hear Ye, Hear Ye

HUM 265.... 7½″ (CE)

Produced with 4 and 5 trademarks. Change was made in mid-production year.

Annual Plate, 1973 Globe Trotter

HUM 266.... 7½″ (CE)

HUM 264   Annual Plate, 1971 Heavenly Angel

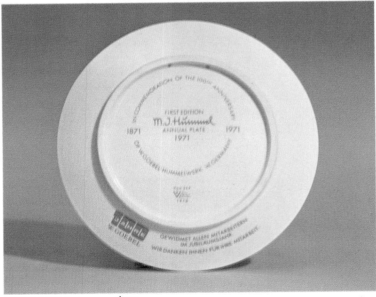

HUM 264   rear view

HUM 265   Annual Plate, 1972 Hear Ye, Hear Ye

HUM 266   Annual Plate, 1973 Globe Trotter

Annual Plate, 1974 Goose Girl

> HUM 267 . . . . 7½″ (CE)

Annual Plate, 1975 Ride Into Christmas

> HUM 268 . . . . 7½″ (CE)

Annual Plate, 1976 Apple Tree Girl

> HUM 269 . . . . 7½″ (CE)

Annual Plate, 1977 Apple Tree Boy

> HUM 270 . . . . 7½″ (CE)

Notice the picture on the 1977 plate closely. The one shown here is an early sample piece. Before production was commenced, the boy's shoes were changed to a slightly different angle and the boy's stockings were reversed (his right one is higher than the left in most known examples.). If your plate is exactly like this picture, you have a rare plate!

HUM 267   Annual Plate, 1974 Goose Girl

HUM 268   Annual Plate, 1975 Ride Into Christmas

HUM 269   Annual Plate, 1976 Apple Tree Girl

HUM 270   Annual Plate, 1977 Apple Tree Boy

171

Annual Plate, 1978 Happy Pastime
    HUM 271 . . . . 7½″ (CE)

Annual Plate, 1979 Singing Lesson
    HUM 272 . . . . 7½″

Annual Plate, 1980 School Girl
    HUM 273 . . . . 7½″

Annual Plate, 1981 Umbrella Boy
    Hum 274 . . . . 7½″

Annual Plate, 1982 Umbrella Girl
    HUM 275 . . . . 7½″

Annual Plate, 1983 Postman
    HUM 276 . . . . 7½″

Annual Plate, 1984 Little Helper
    HUM 277 . . . . 7½″

Annual Plate, 1985 Chick Girl
    HUM 278 . . . . 7½″

Annual Plate, 1986 Playmates
    HUM 279 . . . . 7½″

HUM 271　Annual Plate, 1978 Happy Pastime

HUM 272　Annual Plate, 1979 Singing Lesson

HUM 273　Annual Plate, 1980 School Girl

HUM 274   Annual Plate, 1981 Umbrella Boy

HUM 277   Annual Plate, 1984 Little Helper

HUM 275   Annual Plate, 1982 Umbrella Girl

HUM 278   Annual Plate, 1985 Chick Girl

HUM 276   Annual Plate, 1983 Postman

HUM 279   Annual Plate, 1986 Playmates

**Anniversary Plate, 1975
Stormy Weather**
   HUM 280. . . . 10″ (CE)

**Anniversary Plate, 1980
Ring Around The Rosie
(two girls only)**
   HUM 281. . . . 10″

Bird Watcher
   HUM 300. . . . . 5″
   56

First sold in U. S. in 1979. At
one time called "Tenderness".
Has incised 1956 copyright
date. An early sample of this
figure was produced in 1954 by
Gerhard Skrobek and was assigned the number HUM 233
(CN).

Christmas Angel
   HUM 301. . . . 6¼″ (PFE)
Originally called "Delivery
Angel". An early sample model
of this figure was sculptured by
Theo R. Menzenbach in 1957.
It reportedly was not approved
by the Siessen Convent for production. The sample model in
our collection has an early
"stylized" trademark (3) and an
incised 1957 copyright date.

Concentration
   HUM 302. . . . 5″ (PFE)
Originally called "Knit One,
Purl Two". Girl similar to
HUM 255 (Stitch in Time).

Arithmetic Lesson
   HUM 303. . . . 5¼″ (PFE)
Originally called "School Lesson". Notice similarity—boy
from HUM 170 (School Boys)
and girl from HUM 177
(School Girls).

HUM 280   Anniversary Plate, 1975 Stormy Weather

HUM 281   Anniversary Plate, 1980 Ring Around The Rosie

HUM 300 Bird Watcher

HUM 302 Concentration

HUM 301 Christmas Angel

HUM 303 Arithmetic Lesson

The Artist
HUM 304 . . . . 5½″
④⑤⑥

First introduced to the U.S. market in 1971. Has 1955 copyright date.

The Builder
HUM 305 . . . . 5½″
③④⑤⑥

First introduced to the U.S. market in 1963. Has a 1955 incised copyright date.

Little Bookkeeper
HUM 306 . . . . 4¾″
③④⑤⑥

First introduced in the U.S. market in 1962. Has a 1955 incised copyright date.

Good Hunting!
HUM 307 . . . . 5″
③④⑤⑥

First introduced to the U.S. market in 1962. Has a 1955 incised copyright date. Slightly restyled in recent years. Hat, brush, collar, hair and position of binoculars have some variations.

Little Tailor
HUM 308 . . . . 5¼″ to 5¾″
④⑤⑥

First introduced to the U.S. market in 1972. Early model on the right has a 1955 incised copyright date. Restyled model on the left has a 1972 incised copyright date.

With Loving Greetings
HUM 309 . . . . 3¼″ (PFE)
Originally called "Greetings From".

HUM 304   The Artist

HUM 305   The Builder

HUM 306   Little Bookkeeper

HUM 307   Good Hunting!

HUM 308   Little Tailor
      New style   Old style

HUM 309   With Loving Greetings

Searching Angel, Wall Plaque
HUM 310 . . . . 4¼″ x 3¼″
⑤⑥

First introduced to the U. S. market in 1979. At one time called "Angelic Concern". Has incised 1955 copyright date.

Kiss Me!
HUM 311 . . . . 6″ to 6¼″
③④⑤⑥

First introduced to the U. S. market in 1961. Has a 1955 incised copyright date. Restyled in late 1960's at the request of the convent. The doll was redesigned to look more like a doll instead of a child. Both styles can be found with the 4 trademark.

Honey Lover
HUM 312 . . . . 3¾″ (PFE)
Originally called "In the Jam Pot".

Sunny Morning
HUM 313 . . . . 3¾″ (PFE)
Originally called "Slumber Serenade".

Confidentially
HUM 314 . . . . 5¼″ to 5¾″
④⑤⑥

First introduced to the U. S. market in 1972. Early models have a 1955 incised copyright date. Restyled model has a 1972 incised copyright date. Completely restyled with new stand and tie added to boy.

Mountaineer
HUM 315 . . . . 5″
③④⑤⑥

First introduced to the U. S. market at the N. Y. World's Fair in 1964. Has a 1955 incised copyright date.

HUM 310   Searching Angel, Wall Plaque

HUM 311   Kiss Me!   New style   Old style

HUM 312   Honey Lover

HUM 314   Confidentially   Old style on left

HUM 315   Mountaineer

HUM 313   Sunny Morning

Relaxation
     HUM 316.... 4″ (PFE)
Originally called "Nightly Ritual".

Not For You!
     HUM 317.... 5½″
     ③④⑤⑥
First introduced to the U. S. market in 1961. Has a 1955 incised copyright date. Some catalogues and price lists show size as 6″.

Art Critic
     HUM 318.... 5½″ (PFE)

Doll Bath
     HUM 319.... 5″
     ③④⑤⑥
First introduced to the U. S. market in 1962. Has a 1956 incised copyright date. Has been restyled with the new textured finish.

The Professor
     HUM 320.... 5¾″ (PFE)

Wash Day
     HUM 321.... 5½″ to 6″
     ③④⑤⑥
First introduced to the U. S. market in 1963. Has a 1957 incised copyright date. Older pieces slightly larger.

HUM 316   Relaxation

HUM 317   Not For You!

HUM 318   Art Critic

HUM 320   The Professor

HUM 319   Doll Bath

HUM 321   Wash Day

Little Pharmacist
HUM 322 .... 5¾″ to 6″
③④⑤⑥

First introduced to the U. S. market in 1962. Has a 1955 incised copyright date. Older models are slightly larger. Variation on label of bottle: Rizinusol (German, for vitamins) and Castor Oil.

Merry Christmas, Wall Plaque
HUM 323 .... 5″x3½″
⑤⑥

First introduced to the U. S. market in 1979. Has incised 1955 copyright date.

At The Fence
HUM 324 .... 4¾″ (PFE)
Originally called "The Other Side of the Fence".

Helping Mother
HUM 325 .... 5″ (PFE)
Originally called "Mother's Aid". Similar to HUM 133 "Mother's Helper". First sample painted in 1956. Has incised 1955 copyright date.

Being Punished, Wall Plaque
HUM 326 .... 4″x5″ (PFE)
Originally called "Naughty Boy". Has hole on back for hanging as plaque or will sit upright on base. Has a 1955 incised copyright date on back. First sample painted in 1957.

The Run-A-Way
HUM 327 .... 5¼″
④⑤⑥

First introduced to the U. S. market in 1972. Early model has a 1955 incised copyright date. Restyled model has a 1972 incised copyright date. Completely restyled with new finish and variations in location of basket, hat and shoes. Slight color variations.

HUM 322　Little Pharmacist

HUM 323　Merry Christmas, Wall Plaque

HUM 324   At The Fence

HUM 326   Being Punished, Wall Plaque

HUM 325   Helping Mother

HUM 327   The Run-A-Way
Old style   New style

Carnival
HUM 328 . . . . 5¾″ to 6″
③④⑤⑥

First introduced to the U. S. market in 1963. Early model with full bee trademark has a 1955 incised copyright date. Later models have a 1957 incised copyright date. Older piece slightly larger with minor variations.

Off To School
HUM 329 . . . . 5″ (PFE)
Originally called "Kindergarten Romance".

Baking Day
HUM 330 . . . . 5¼″ (PFE)
Originally called "Kneading Dough".

Crossroads
HUM 331 . . . . 6¾″
④⑤⑥

First introduced to the U. S. market in 1972. Has a 1955 incised copyright date. Early sample models had the trombone reversed, which is extremely rare.

HUM 328   Carnival

HUM 329   Off To School

HUM 330   Baking Day

HUM 331   Crossroads   Old style   New style

HUM 331   rear view   Old style   New style

Soldier Boy
HUM 332.... 5¾" to 6"
③④⑤⑥

First introduced to the U. S. market in 1963. Early model with full bee trademark has a 1955 incised copyright date. Later models have a 1957 incised copyright date. Older pieces slightly larger. Older models have red ornament on hat while newer ones have blue.

Blessed Event
HUM 333.... 5¼" to 5½"
③④⑤⑥

First introduced to the U. S. market at the N. Y. World's Fair in 1964. Found with either 1955 or 1957 incised copyright dates.

Homeward Bound
HUM 334.... 5¼"
④⑤⑥

First introduced to the U. S. market in 1971. Found with either 1955 or 1956 incised copyright dates in early models. Restyled in 1975 with new textured finish and without support pedestal under the goat. Current model has 1975 incised copyright date. Note red line on base of older model, which indicates this is on artist's sample piece for use as a model while painting current figurines.

Lucky Boy
HUM 335.... 5¾" to 6"
(PFE)
Originally called "Fair Prizes".

Close Harmony
HUM 336.... 5¼" to 5½"
③④⑤⑥

First introduced to the U. S. market in 1963. Found with either 1955, 1956 or 1957 incised copyright dates. Current production has been restyled but bears the 1955 incised copyright date. Older models have variations in girl's hair style and position of stockings.

HUM 332   Soldier Boy

HUM 333   Blessed Event

HUM 334   Homeward Bound
Old style   New style

HUM 335   Lucky Boy

HUM 336   Close Harmony Old style   New style

Cinderella
HUM 337 . . . . 4½″
④⑤⑥

First introduced to the U. S. market in 1972. Early models have a 1958 incised copyright date. Restyled model has a 1972 incised copyright date. Completely restyled with new textured finish and girl's eyes closed. Older model has eyes open.

Birthday Cake, Candle Holder
HUM 338 . . . . 3¾″ (PFE)
Originally called "A Birthday Wish". Sample model has full bee trademark and stamped 1956 copyright date. First sample painted in 1956.

Behave!
HUM 339 . . . . 5⅓″ to 5¾″ (PFE)
Originally called "Walking Her Dog".

Letter To Santa Claus
HUM 340 . . . . 7¼″
④⑤⑥

First introduced to the U. S. market in 1971. Early sample models have a full bee trademark with a stamped 1957 copyright date. Early "stylized" trademark piece has incised 1956 copyright date. Current production has been completely restyled with new textured finish and color variations in girl's hat and leggings. First sample painted in 1957.

Birthday Present
HUM 341 . . . . 5″ to 5⅓″ (PFE)
Originally called "The Birthday Present".

HUM 337 **Cinderella**   New style   Old style

HUM 338   **Birthday Cake, Candle Holder**

HUM 339 Behave!

HUM 341 Birthday Present

HUM 340 Letter To Santa Claus New style   Old style

Mischief Maker
   HUM 342 . . . . 5″
   ④⑤⑥

First introduced to the U. S. market in 1972. Found with either 1958 or 1960 incised copyright dates.

Christmas Song
   HUM 343 . . . . 6½″ (PFE)
Originally called "Singing Angel".

Feathered Friends
   HUM 344 . . . . 4¾″
   ④⑤⑥

First introduced to the U. S. market in 1972. Has a 1956 incised copyright date.

A Fair Measure
   HUM 345 . . . . 5½″ to 5¾″
   ④⑤⑥

First introduced to the U. S. market in 1972. Early full bee sample pieces have a stamped 1957 copyright date. Early production models have 1956 incised copyright date. Completely restyled with new textured finish with boy's eyes looking down and weights on scale reversed. Current model has a 1972 incised copyright date. First sample painted in 1957.

Smart Little Sister
   HUM 346 . . . . 4¾″
   ③④⑤⑥

First introduced to the U. S. market in 1962. Has a 1956 incised copyright date.

HUM 342   Mischief Maker

HUM 343   Christmas Song

HUM 344 Feathered Friends

HUM 346 Smart Little Sister

HUM 345 A Fair Measure New style   Old style

**Adventure Bound, the
Seven Swabians**
    HUM 347 . . . . 7½″x8¼″
    ④⑤⑥

First introduced to the U. S.
market in 1971. Has a 1957
incised copyright date. The
original clay model was sculpted by Theo R. Menzenbach in
1957. Early sample has a "full
bee" trademark and was painted
in October 1957.

Ring Around The Rosie
    HUM 348 . . . . 6¾″
    ③④⑤⑥

The original clay model was
sculpted by Gerhard Skrobek,
current master modeller at the
factory, in 1957. First introduced to the U. S. market in the
early 1960's. Incised on the bottom: © by W. Goebel, Oeslau
1957. The older model is
slightly larger.

The Florist
    HUM 349 . . . . 7″ to 7½″
    (PFE)
Originally called "Flower
Lover".

On Holiday
    HUM 350 . . . . 4¼″ (PFE)
Originally called "Holiday
Shopper".

HUM 347   Adventure Bound, the Seven Swabians

HUM 348   Ring Around The Rosie

HUM 349   The Florist

HUM 350   On Holiday

The Botanist
> **HUM 351 . . . . 4″ to 4¼″**
> **(PFE)**

Originally called "Remembering".

Sweet Greetings
> **HUM 352 . . . . 4¼″ (PFE)**

Originally called "Musical Good-Morning".

Spring Dance
> **HUM 353/0 . 5¼″**
> **353/I . . 6¾″**

First introduced to the U. S. market in 1964. Has a 1963 incised copyright date on both sizes. The small size (353/0) has been considered rare but is again in current production with the 5 and 6 trademarks.

Holy Water Font, Angel With Lantern
> **HUM 354 A . . 3¼″x5″**
> **(PFE)**

Early sample model has incised number 354.

Holy Water Font, Angel With Trumpet
> **HUM 354 B . . 3¼″x5″**
> **(PFE)**

Early sample model has incised number 355.

Holy Water Font, Angel With Bird and Cross
> **HUM 354 C . . 3¼″x5″**
> **(PFE)**

Early sample model has incised number 356.

HUM 351   The Botanist

HUM 352   Sweet Greetings

HUM 353   Spring Dance

HUM 354 A
Angel With Lantern,
Holy Water Font

HUM 354 B
Angel With Trumpet,
Holy Water Font

HUM 354 C
Angel With Bird and Cross,
Holy Water Font

Autumn Harvest
　　HUM 355 . . . . 5″
　　④⑤⑥

First introduced to the U. S. market in 1972. Has a 1964 incised copyright date.

Gay Adventure
　　HUM 356 . . . . 4¾″
　　④⑤⑥

First introduced to the U. S. market in 1972. Has a 1971 incised copyright date. Slightly restyled with the new textured finish on current models. Early models have different construction on under side of base. Was called "Joyful Adventure" in older catalogs.

Guiding Angel
　　HUM 357 . . . . 2¾″
　　④⑤⑥

First introduced to the U. S. market in 1972. Has a 1960 incised copyright date.

Shining Light
　　HUM 358 . . . . 2¾″
　　④⑤⑥

First introduced to the U. S. Market in 1972. Has a 1960 incised copyright date.

Tuneful Angel
　　HUM 359 . . . . 2¾″
　　④⑤⑥

First introduced to the U. S. market in 1972. Has a 1960 incised copyright date.

Wall Vase, Boy and Girl
　　HUM 360/A . . 4½″x6″
　　③ ? ⑤⑥

Early models incised on back: "© by W. Goebel 1958." Has been considered rare but is again in current production with the 5 and 6 trademarks. New model has been slightly restyled and has copyright date "1958" only incised on back.

(continued)

HUM 355　Autumn Harvest

HUM 356　Gay Adventure

HUM 357   Guiding Angel   **HUM 358   Shining Light**   **HUM 359   Tuneful Angel**

HUM 360/A Wall Vase, Boy and Girl

HUM 360/B   Wall Vase, Boy

HUM 360/C   Wall Vase, Girl

Wall Vase, Boy
  HUM 360/B. . 4½″x6″
  ③ ? ⑤⑥

Early models incised on back: "© by W. Goebel 1958." Has been considered rare but is again in current production with 5 and 6 trademarks. New model has copyright date "1958" only incised on back.

Wall Vase, Girl
  HUM 360/C . 4½″x6″
  ③ ? ⑤⑥

Early models incised on back: "© by W. Goebel 1958." Has been considered rare but is again in current production with 5 and 6 trademarks. On new models, trunk of tree has been slightly restyled and has copyright date "1958" only incised on back.

Favorite Pet
  HUM 361. . . . 4½″
  ③④⑤⑥

First introduced to the U. S. market at the N. Y. World's Fair in 1964. Has a 1960 incised copyright date.

I Forgot
  HUM 362. . . . 5½″ (PFE)
Originally called "Thoughtful".

Big Housecleaning
  HUM 363. . . . 4″
  ④⑤⑥

First introduced to the U. S. market in 1972. Has a 1960 incised copyright date.

Supreme Protection
  HUM 364. . . . 8¾″ to 9″
                  (PFE)
Originally called "Blessed Madonna and Child".

HUM 361   Favorite Pet

HUM 362   I Forgot

HUM 364   Supreme Protection

HUM 363   Big Housecleaning

Littlest Angel
    HUM 365 . . . . 2¼″ to 2¾″
              (PFE)
Originally called "The Wee
Angel".

Flying Angel
    HUM 366 . . . . 3½″
    ④⑤⑥
Has a 1964 incised copyright
date. Produced both in color
and white overglaze. Used as
part of HUM 214 nativity set or
as decorations for Christmas
trees.

Busy Student
    HUM 367 . . . . 4¼″
    ③④⑤⑥
First introduced to the U. S.
market in 1964. Has a 1963
incised copyright date.

Lute Song
    HUM 368 . . . . 5″ (PFE)
Originally called "Lute
Player". Note: this is one girl
from HUM 336 Close Har-
mony.

Follow The Leader
    HUM 369 . . . . 7″
    ④⑤⑥
First introduced to the U. S.
market in 1972. Has a 1964
incised copyright date.

HUM 365   Littlest Angel

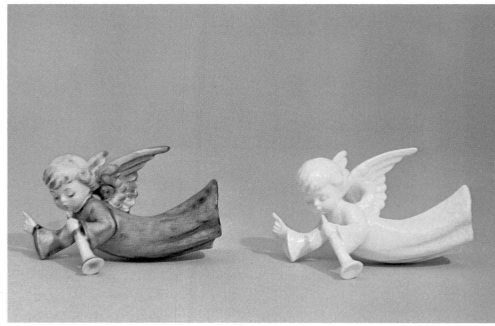

HUM 366   Flying Angel

HUM 367   Busy Student

HUM 369   Follow The Leader

HUM 368   Lute Song

Companions

HUM 370 . . . . **4¼ to 4¾″ (PFE)**

Originally called "Brotherly Love". Designed by Gerhard Skrobek—May 1964.

Daddy's Girls

HUM 371 . . . . **4¾″ (PFE)**

Originally called "Sisterly Love". Designed by Gerhard Skrobek—May 1964.

Blessed Mother

HUM 372 . . . . **10¼″ (PFE)**

Originally called "Virgin Mother and Child". Designed by Gerhard Skrobek—May 1964.

HUM 370 Companions

HUM 371   Daddy's Girls

HUM 372   Blessed Mother

Just Fishing
> HUM 373 . . . . 4¼″x4½″
> **(PFE)**

Originally called "The Fisherman". Designed by Gerhard Skrobek—December 1964.

Lost Stocking
> HUM 374 . . . . 4½″
> **④⑤⑥**

First introduced to the U. S. market in 1972. Has a 1965 incised copyright date. Designed by Gerhard Skrobek—January 1965.

Morning Stroll
> HUM 375 . . . . 4¼″ (PFE)

Originally called "Walking the Baby". Designed by Gerhard Skrobek—November 1964.

Little Nurse
> HUM 376 . . . . 4″ (PFE)

Originally called "First Aid." Designed by Gerhard Skrobek—April 1965.

HUM 373   Just Fishing

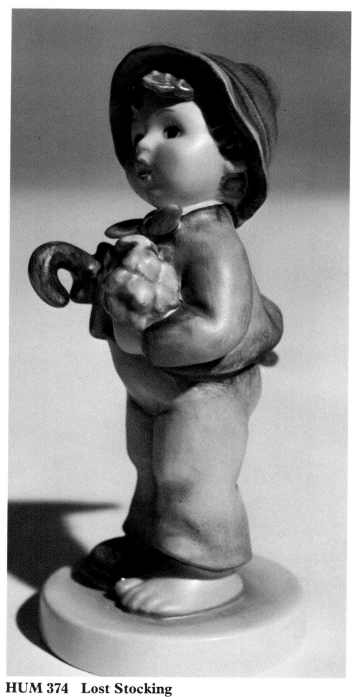

HUM 374   Lost Stocking

HUM 375   Morning Stroll

HUM 376   Little Nurse

Bashful!

    HUM 377 . . . . 4¾″

      ④⑤⑥

First introduced to the U. S. market in 1972. Has a 1966 incised copyright date. Designed by Gerhard Skrobek—January 1966.

Easter Greetings!

    HUM 378 . . . . 5¼″

      ④⑤⑥

First introduced to the U. S. market in 1972. Has a 1971 incised copyright date.

Don't Be Shy

    HUM 379 . . . . 4¼″ to 4½″

      (PFE)

Originally called "One For You—One For Me". Designed by Gerhard Skrobek—February 1966.

Daisies Don't Tell

    HUM 380 . . . . 4½″ to 5″

      (PFE)

Originally called "Does He". Designed by Gerhard Skrobek—February 1966.

HUM 377   Bashful!

HUM 378   Easter Greetings!

HUM 379   Don't Be Shy

HUM 380   Daisies Don't Tell

Flower Vendor
HUM 381.... 5¼″
④⑤⑥

First introduced to the U. S. market in 1972. Has a 1971 incised copyright date.

Visiting An Invalid
HUM 382.... 5″
④⑤⑥

First introduced to the U. S. market in 1972. Has a 1971 incised copyright date.

Going Home
HUM 383.... 4¼″ to 4¾″
(PFE)
Originally called "Fancy Free". Designed by Gerhard Skrobek—November 1966.

Easter Time
HUM 384.... 4″
④⑤⑥

First introduced to the U. S. market in 1972. Has a 1971 incised copyright date. Also called "Easter Playmates" in some catalogues.

Chicken-Licken!
HUM 385.... 4¾″
④⑤⑥

First introduced to the U. S. market in 1972. Has a 1971 incised copyright date.

HUM 381   Flower Vendor

HUM 382   Visiting An Invalid

HUM 384   Easter Time

HUM 383   Going Home

HUM 385   Chicken-Licken!

On Secret Path
   HUM 386 . . . . 5¼″
   ④⑤⑥

First introduced to the U. S. market in 1972. Has a 1971 incised copyright date.

Valentine Gift
   HUM 387 . . . . 5¼″ (CE)

First issued in 1977 for members of the Goebel Collectors' Club. Not sold as an Open Edition. Has a 1972 incised copyright date. Also 5 trademark, W. Germany and 1972 applied by blue decal. Also bears inscription: "EXCLUSIVE SPECIAL EDITION No.1 FOR MEMBERS OF THE GOEBEL COLLECTORS' CLUB" applied by blue decal. Translation of message on heart: "I Love You Very Much".

Little Band, Candle Holder
   HUM 388 . . . . 3″x4¾″
   ④⑤⑥

Candle holder of HUM 389, HUM 390, and HUM 391 on round base. Has a 1968 incised copyright date.

Little Band, Candle Holder on Music Box
   HUM 388/M . 3″x4¾″

Same as HUM 388 but on music box. Variations in type of music box and tunes played.

HUM 386   On Secret Path

HUM 387   Valentine Gift　　　　**HUM 388   Little Band, Candle Holder**

HUM 388/M   Little Band, Candle Holder on Music Box

HUM 389   Girl With Sheet of Music   HUM 390   Boy With Accordion   HUM 391   Girl With Trumpet

Girl With Sheet of Music
 HUM 389 . . . . 2½″
 ❹❺❻

Has a 1968 incised copyright date.

Boy With Accordion
 HUM 390 . . . . 2½″
 ❹❺❻

Has a 1968 incised copyright date.

Girl With Trumpet
 HUM 391 . . . . 2½″
 ❹❺❻

Has a 1968 incised copyright date.

Little Band (on base)
 HUM 392 . . . . 3″x4¾″
 ❹❺❻

Same as HUM 388 but without socket for candle. Has a 1968 incised copyright date.

Little Band on Music Box
 HUM 392/M . .3″x4¾″
Same as HUM 392 but on music box. Variations in type of music box and tunes played.

Holy Water Font, Dove
 HUM 393 . . . . 2¾″x4¼″
 (PFE)

Designed by Gerhard Skrobek—June 1968.

Timid Little Sister
 HUM 394 . . . . 6½″ (PFE)
Designed by Gerhard Skrobek—February 1972.

HUM 392   Little Band (on base)

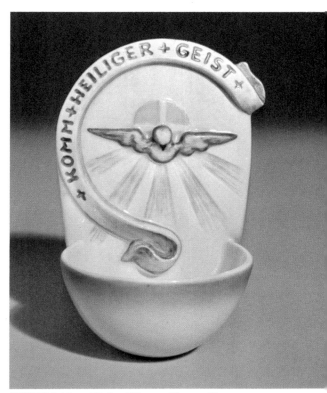

HUM 393   Holy Water Font, Dove

HUM 392/M   Little Band on Music Box

HUM 394   Timid Little Sister

Shepherd Boy
HUM 395 . . . . 6″ to 6½″
(PFE)
Originally called "Young Shepherd". Designed by Gerhard Skrobek—February 1971.

Ride Into Christmas
HUM 396 . . . . 5¾″
❹❺❻
First introduced to the U. S. market in 1972. Has a 1971 incised copyright date. Designed by Gerhard Skrobek—December 1970.

Smiling Through, Plaque
HUM 690 . . . . 5¾″
First issued in 1978 for members of the Goebel Collectors' Club. Not sold as an open edition. Nothing incised on back. Applied by blue decal: "EXCLUSIVE SPECIAL EDITION No.2 HUM 690 FOR MEMBERS OF THE Goebel Collectors' Club". Also has 5 trademark, and W. Germany 1978. No holes are provided for hanging.

Annual Bell, 1978 Let's Sing
HUM 700 . . . . 6″ (CE)
First edition in series of annual bells. Has 1978 in red on back along with the "M.I. Hummel" signature. "HUM 700" affixed by decal along with 5 trademark on inside of bell.

Annual Bell, 1979 Farewell
HUM 701 . . . . 6″
Has 1979 in red on back along with the "M.I. Hummel" signature. "HUM 701" affixed by decal along with 5 trademark on inside of bell.

HUM 395   Shepherd Boy   HUM 396   Ride Into Christmas

HUM 690   Smiling Through, Plaque

HUM 700   Annual Bell, 1978 Let's Sing

HUM 690   rear view

HUM 701   Annual Bell, 1979 Farewell

HUM 809 **HUM 807** **HUM 832** **HUM 854**

HUM 904 **HUM 806** **HUM 841** **HUM 851**

INTERNATIONAL "M. I. HUMMEL" FIGURINES

The eight figurines at left are the original "Hungarian" figurines discovered early in 1976 by a man in Vienna. He had acquired them from a lady in Budapest, who had purchased them at the weekly "flea market"—one at a time, over a six-month period. He in turn sold them to collector Robert L. Miller, a supermarket owner in Eaton, Ohio, as a gift for his wife Ruth.

"Hummel" figurines have always been typically German, have always had German-style dress or costumes. In 1940, the W. Goebel company decided to produce a line of "M. I. Hummel" figurines in the national dress of other countries. Sister M. I. Hummel made many sketches of children in their native costumes. Modellers Reinhold Unger and Arthur Möller then turned the sketches into the adorable figurines you see on the following pages. In consequence of the events of the Second World War, production of the series of international figurines was not started. After the discovery in 1976 of the "Hungarian" figurines, a thorough search of the factory was conducted, including the checking and rechecking of old records. Twenty-four sample models were found and are pictured here. Most of the people involved in the original project are no longer living, therefore the information contained here may not be absolutely accurate or complete. Author/collector Miller states "I feel that more rare finds may be made in the future. Happy hunting!"

HUM 806 Bulgarian

HUM 808 Bulgarian

HUM 809 Bulgarian

HUM 810 Bulgarian

HUM 810 Bulgarian

HUM 811 Bulgarian

HUM 812 Serbian

HUM 813   Serbian

HUM 825   Swedish

HUM 825   Swedish

HUM 824   Swedish

HUM 831   Slovak

HUM 832   Slovak

HUM 833   Slovak

HUM 841   Czech

HUM 842   Czech

HUM 851   Hungarian

HUM 852   Hungarian

HUM 852   Hungarian

HUM 853   Hungarian

HUM 854   Hungarian

HUM 904   Serbian

HUM 947   Serbian

HUM 968   Serbian

221

CHAPTER
7: HISTORY & EXPLANATION OF MARKS & SYMBOLS

"Incise Crown"

"Stamped Crown"

1935–1949

M.J.Hümmel ©

1935–1955

Made in
U.S.-Zone
Germany.

U.S. Zone
Germany.

U.S.-Zone
Germany

U.S.-Zone
Germany.

U.S. Zone
Germany.

Made in
U.S. Zone

Made in U.S. Zone
Germany.

U.S. Zone

1946–1948

The "Wide Crown—WG" trademark was used on the first "M.I. Hummel" figurines produced in 1935. On the earliest figurines it was incised on the bottom of the base along with the "M.I. Hummel" signature on the top or side of the base. Between 1935 and 1955, the company occasionally used a© ⌣ mark on the side or top of the base of some models. It is seen occasionally appearing to the right of the "M.I. Hummel" signature. The "Crown" appears either incised or stamped. When both are used on the same piece it is known as a "Double Crown" mark.

From 1946 through 1948 it was necessary to add the stamped words "Made in U.S. Zone Germany". This mark was used within various types of frames or without a frame, underglazed or stamped over the glaze in black ink.

In 1950, Goebel wished in some way to pay tribute to the fine artistry of Sister M.I. Hummel, whose untimely death in 1946 had deprived the world of a style unique yet far-reaching in its appeal. They succeeded by radically changing the trademark, instituting the use of a "bee" flying high within a "V". (Hummel means bumble bee in German, and the "V" stands for "Verkaufsgesellschaft" or distribution company.) This mark, known as the "Full Bee" trademark, was used until 1955 and appeared—sometimes both incised and underglazed—in black or blue and occasionally in green or magenta. In addition, the stamp "Germany" and later "West Germany" appeared. Frequently an ® will appear beside the trademark. This stands for "Registered" and has no special significance—it neither adds nor detracts from the value of the figurine.

Sometimes the molds were produced with a lightly incised circle on the bottom of the base in which the trademark was centered. The circle has no significance other than as a target for the location of the decal. Some current production figurines still have this incised circle even though it is no longer used for that purpose.

Always searching for a mark that would blend esthetics with professionalism, the company continued to modify the trademark; in 1956, the company—still using the "bee" inside the "V"—made the bee smaller, this time with its wing tips parallel with the top of the "V". In 1957, the bee remained, although once again, it was seen rising slightly above the "V". In 1958, the bee was smaller still and it flew deep within the "V", reflecting the changing trends of modern design. The year 1959 saw the beginning of stylization and the wings of the bee became sharply angular.

In 1960, the completely "Stylized Bee with V" mark came into use, appearing with "W. Germany". The "Stylized Bee" trademark was used in one form or another until 1979. In addition to its appearance with "W. Germany" to the right (1960–1963), it appeared poised above the "W. Germany" (1960–1972), and to the left of the "Three Line Mark" (mid-1960's to 1972).

It is difficult to pinpoint the exact date that the "Three Line Mark" was first used. It was used intermittently and sometimes concurrently with the small "stylized 1960–1972 mark". It was used more extensively in the late 1960's and early 1970's and was the most prominent trademark in use prior to the introduction of the "Goebel Bee" trademark.

It became apparent that the public was equating the "V and Bee" mark only with "Hummel," assuming that every item marked this way was an "M.I. Hummel" item and did not include the full scope of Goebel products. It was therefore decided to experiment further with marks. In 1972, satisfied that it had arrived at a mark designating a quality Goebel product, the company began the use of a printed "Goebel with the Stylized V and Bee" poised between the letters "b" and "e".

Occasionally a "Hummel" figurine is without a trademark for practical reasons. There simply is not room for these marks to be placed on these figurines without affecting their appearance. In such a case the company applies the Goebel trademark by means of a sticker.

Since 1976, the Goebel trademark on "Hummel" figurines has been affixed by a decal on top of the glaze and then fired again. Before 1976, the decal was affixed under the glaze. It would be possible, therefore, to see two figurines on the primary market with differing decals.

In 1979, it was announced that the stylized bee was being dropped and that only the name *Goebel* will appear. In addition, the year of production will be shown on the base next to the initials of the chief decorator. These changes will be incorporated into production as existing

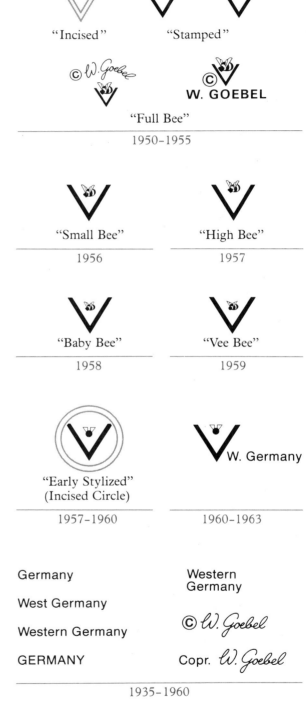

"Incised" "Stamped"

© W. Goebel © W. GOEBEL

"Full Bee"

1950–1955

"Small Bee" "High Bee"

1956 1957

"Baby Bee" "Vee Bee"

1958 1959

"Early Stylized" (Incised Circle) W. Germany

1957–1960 1960–1963

Germany Western Germany

West Germany

Western Germany © W. Goebel

GERMANY Copr. W. Goebel

1935–1960

Evolution of Trademark "Goebel Bee"
in use since 1972

Goebel
W. Germany

1979 Current Trademark

stocks of figurines are exhausted.

When speaking of a production era, let us say for example, 1950–55, the "Full Bee" period, it is always possible to have some slight production overlap. Collectors have written to the authors saying that they recall having purchased their "Full Bee" pieces in West Germany in 1949, while we state that the "Full Bee" did not appear until 1950. How could that have happened? In order for Goebel craftsmen to implement the trademark changeover by the desired date, in this case, 1950, it was necessary to begin production of the "Full Bee" pieces in 1949. Some of the "M.I. Hummel" figurines bearing the "Full Bee" mark were accidently placed in shipments, finding their way to the marketplace ahead of schedule. This occurrence may have taken place during other periods of trademark changeover, but it does not indicate a "rare" or unusually valuable "M. I. Hummel" figurine.

The above information is a concise documentation of all W. Goebel trademarks authorized for use on "M.I. Hummel" figurines. In searching for accurate documentation on all W. Goebel trademarks used in conjunction with "M.I. Hummel" figurines, the authors made a thorough investigation of the W. Goebel archive and queried the world's leading collectors on the subject. But, as is the case with other aspects of "M.I. Hummel" figurine collecting, it is always possible that a few rare and undocumented variations may exist.

This is the figurine identification number. It is the official means of identifying all figurines produced by W. Goebel. Here, for example, we find HUM 396, otherwise known as Ride into Christmas. Since it has only been manufactured in one size (5¾″) it does not carry a size designator. Size designators appear to the right of the figurine identification number, set off by a slash.

The copyright © to the left of the W. Goebel trademark indicates that this particular figurine is protected by U.S. copyright laws.

This incised number cannot help you to identify or date your figurine. It is simply a control number used by W. Goebel's molding department during periodic quality checks.

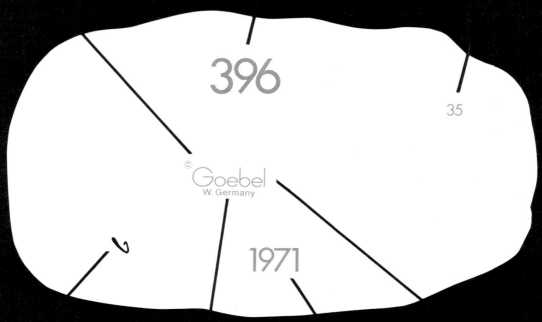

This painted and over-glazed symbol cannot help you to identify or date your figurine. It is the symbol used by one of W. Goebel's master painters to approve the artistry of the figurine during one of the many quality control checks.

The "W. Germany," though sitting directly below the W. Goebel trademark, is not part of the trademark design. It is present to legally establish the country of origin of the "M.I. Hummel" figurines for export purposes.

This is the current W. Goebel trademark. It is used on "M.I. Hummel" figurines and other collectors objects.

This date, below the W. Goebel trademark, indicates the year of copyright publication of the particular figurine model.

Collectors of "M.I. Hummel" figurines frequently want to know why there are variations involving sizes, colors, names, designations, and the actual appearances of differing models with the same number.

The overall answer should not be surprising: Just as with stamps, coins, and limited editions, there are changes and errors during production which are often highly appealing to serious collectors. For example, "inverted" stamps and "mint error" coins are legendary among collectors and auctioneers. In fact, it is often a collector's dream to one day discover an example which is different from the norm.

"M.I. Hummel" figurines are no exception. Prolific collectors scour the world looking for unusual and obvious variations. Some are errors, some are not. That is why this chapter has been assembled, as a *general guide* to *known* variations and "mint errors" involving "M.I. Hummel" figurines.

Still, the reader must remember that additional variations and errors are bound to be found in future "M.I. Hummel" collecting, just as the U.S. Mint will still turn out the occasional oddity. These discoveries add a new dimension to every collector's fund of information.

Here, now, are general guidelines.

COLOR VARIATIONS

Variations in the colors of "M.I. Hummel" figurines have occurred for a variety of reasons, which fall into three basic categories: unrecorded variations, authorized production changes, and simple aging.

Unrecorded variations have been noted by many collectors, especially in the area of madonnas and other religious figurines. The majority of these variations are in white overglaze, white bisque, and the fully painted figurines. The highly detailed hand painting process finds no two artists with exactly the same style. As a result, minor unrecorded variations may occur. Though white overglaze and white bisque variations appear throughout the entire "M.I. Hummel" collection, they are considered to be very rare. Unrecorded variations are those not authorized for production by W. Goebel.

Production and model changes have been continually taking place since "M.I. Hummel" figurines first appeared on the market in 1935. These changes can concern themselves with color, design, or size. They can also come about through development of new ceramic paints by the W. Goebel chemical laboratory.

For example, in efforts to brighten the appearance of the figurine faces, W. Goebel developed a brighter red paint for the lips of the figurines. Individual cases of color change always have tended to brighten the appearance of a particular figurine, and in general, the development of new metallic oxide paints since the mid-1950s has set figurines of more recent manufacture apart from their older counterparts.

Aging of old figurines occurs due to the chemical composition of their ceramic mass, and due to the atmospheric conditions of the area where the figurines are kept. The basic molecular compositon of the various clays, kaolins, feldspars, and quartzes employed in the milling of the ceramic mass change from pit to pit, mine to mine, and region to region. As a result, colors tend to dull or mellow on figurines manufactured prior to the mid-1950s. Developments by W. Goebel chemists since this period have enabled the factory to produce "M.I. Hummel" figurines and other collectors items in bright, exciting colors which offer lasting beauty that will not fade, dull, or mellow for either chemical or atmospheric reasons.

NAME VARIATION

The names originally applied to some "M.I. Hummel" figurines in early catalogs have been changed. The reason for this was a switch from pure translation to transliteration, that is translating according to the idea or theme rather than the literal meaning of the original German. For example, figurine HUM 142 Apple Tree Boy was originally called Fall in English. Since name changes do not directly affect the figurines themselves, they are considered of minor importance to serious collectors.

MODEL VARIATION

Model variations, both authorized and unknown, are of special interest to serious collectors. The reason for this is that they offer the collector the opportunity to possess unique figurines. These rarities are, in most cases, the result of production changes during the early years of their appearance or unknown errors during the production process. Because of the widespread interest in these unique figurines, a substantial portion of this chapter is devoted to a full-color visual record of those pieces known to exist.

BASE VARIATION

Occasionally, collectors will come across two figurines identical except for the bases. From time to time, the W. Goebel firm has changed the design of its "M.I. Hummel" figurine bases for better support and visual compatibility with the figurines themselves. Also, a figurine base will often change if a particular model is redesigned. Contrary to rumor, the W. Goebel firm has never maintained stockpiles of standard "M.I. Hummel" figurine bases. Each figurine has a specially designed base to complement its style.

SIZE
DESIGNATORS

Since the beginning of production, "M.I. Hummel" figurines have been manufactured in numerous official sizes. Some models have been made in more sizes than others, but there is no single reason for this.

As a result of the varying sizes, a marking system has evolved over the years to designate variations within a particular model. In addition to officially authorized variations in size, there are many examples of "mold growth" figurines made during the pre-1954 era when plaster of paris was used for working models. Since 1954, the use of acrylic resin for modeling has led to greater uniformity in the figurines themselves.

When each model is first made, the first size decided upon for production becomes the "standard" of that model. On early figurines, this was designated on the bottom by a "0" appearing after a slash following the model number. For example, HUM 47 (Goose Girl—first made in the 1930s) in the standard size (4¾″) has the marking 47/0. But not all standard sizes of all figurines use the "0".

The designation "0" appeared with the first figurines in 1935 and was used for the last time with HUM 218 Birthday Serenade, after which it was dropped as a designation of the standard size for all subsequent model numbers. (Note: there has been one exception—HUM 353 Spring Dance, which has been manufactured in a 353/0 size. As a result, this figurine has earned a reputation among collectors as a rare model.) No substitution for the "0" was made. Thus, no figurines numbered higher than HUM 218 carry any designation for the standard size of each.

Prior to its elimination from the size designation system, the "0" appeared to the right of the Arabic number markings used to designate models smaller than the standard size. In the case of larger variations of the same model, the "0" never followed the Roman numerals. The subsequent designator is now usually either a Roman numeral or an Arabic number.

Figurines larger than the "0" size are designated by Roman numerals in ascending order from I to X. Size I is therefore larger than size "0" with the general rule being that the larger the Roman numeral, the greater the size of the figurine. This does not guarantee that two figurines of the same model number with the same size designation—II for example—will be of the same height due to the slight growth of the old plaster working models used prior to 1954. It is also possible that a figurine model has been redesigned, re-master molded, reapproved by the Siessen Convent, and come out of production different in size than its older counterpart of the same size designation. In the past two decades, the W. Goebel firm has made great strides in the area of standardization of its "M.I. Hummel" figurines, but due to the growth of the old plaster of paris working models and the enormous redesigning effort that took place when the firm began gearing up for production after the end of the Second World War, it is possible that a collector will run into minor size variations within the same model that have the same size designation.

Figurines smaller than the "0" size are designated by Arabic numbers in ascending order from 1 upward. This designation generally appears on the bottom of the base and to the right of the model number, set off by a slash. In some special cases, however, the Arabic number will precede the model number. The rule is the larger the Arabic number, the smaller the figurine size. After the Arabic size designation there is another slash, followed by a zero. The presence of this zero to the right of the designation indicates that the figurine in question is smaller than the "0" size. Roman numeral indicators *are not* followed by a zero.

Here are a couple of examples:

195/2/0—"M.I. Hummel" figurine 195, "Barnyard Hero"
size 4 inches

195/I—"M.I. Hummel" figurine 195, "Barnyard Hero"
size 5½ inches

Note that HUM 195/2/0 is smaller than its counterpart, HUM 195/I, which has a Roman numeral size designation.

The size designation system can be best demonstrated by this key:

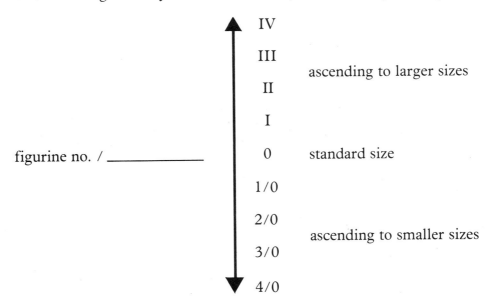

In understanding the size designation system of "M.I. Hummel" figurines, it is important to remember that the designations apply differently to each specific figurine model, but that generally larger and smaller sizes of the same model are specified by the designation key.

VARIATIONS: Candleholders and Boxes

"M.I. Hummel" candy boxes, music boxes, and candleholders differ from the figurines because the size of the candleholder or the size of the box appears *before* the figurine model number, or to the left of it.

Example: HUM 110/0 is the figurine "Let's Sing," but HUM III/110 is the box "Let's Sing" based upon the design of HUM 110.

SPECIAL CASES: Numbers and Markings Which May Confuse

a.) HUM 78, "The Infant of Krumbad," has been produced in three finishes: matte (brownish bisque), full color and white overglaze. It has been given color designation numbers, which appear *after* the size designation and are preceded by a slash as follows:

HUM 78/ size / paint

The paint numbers will be 83 for matte bisque, 11 for full color or W for white overglaze. Color designators are never incised on the figurines but are used only in catalogues, price lists or other literature.

b.) Markings that appear on the base bottoms of some "M.I. Hummel" figurines in underglaze in the form of initials or small numbers and may confuse collectors, indicate the numerical or signature code of a particular molding department supervisor or master painter who supervised that phase of the figurine manufacture. These markings in no way refer to the year of production, model number, or size designation.

Can you determine the markings on the base of this figurine?

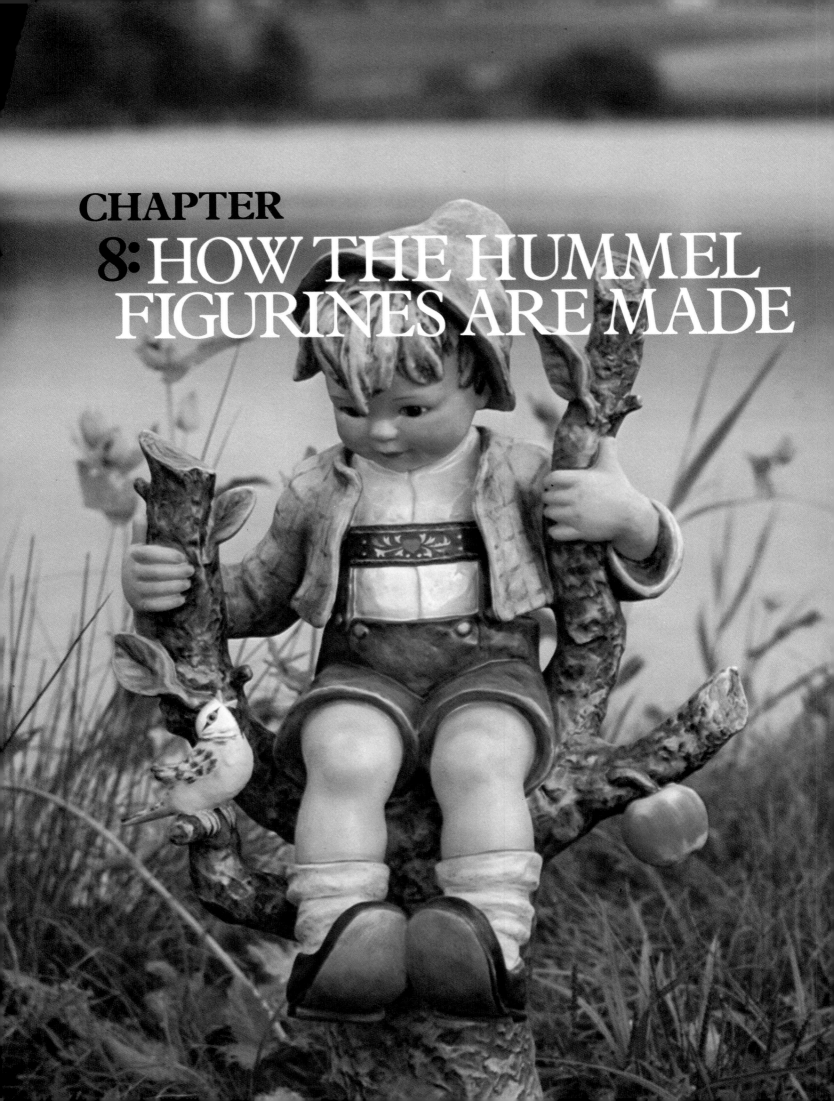

Good collectors should have a thorough knowledge of their collectibles, valuing the work that went into making them just as they value the objects themselves. In a world where handcraftsmanship is rapidly disappearing, the W. Goebel firm, sole manufacturers of "M.I. Hummel" figurines and plates under exclusive license from the Siessen Convent, has continued to follow the two-century-old tradition of porcelain and ceramic manufacture that was developed in its Thuringian homeland shortly before the American Revolution. A work force of 1,500 operates as a team at the Goebel factory in the town of Rödental to produce "M.I. Hummel" figurines, plates, and other collector items. The manufacturing process of an "M.I. Hummel" figurine involves over 700 painstaking hand operations and twenty-five quality control checks. To better understand what goes into the making of an "M.I. Hummel" figurine, it is essential to describe its manufacture step-by-step.

I MODELING

The basis for the creation of an "M.I. Hummel" figurine is the collection of drawings and sketches by Sister Maria Innocentia Hummel provided to the W. Goebel firm under special agreement with the Siessen Convent. W. Goebel's chief designer then studies Sister Innocentia's artwork and begins the time-consuming process of creating a clay model that rigidly conforms in color and form to Sister Innocentia's design. Once the original clay model is completed, it is presented to the Siessen Convent for approval. Sometimes the Convent will ask the designer to make minor changes, other times not. After the model has been approved by the Convent, the design must be officially authorized by the directors of the W. Goebel firm for release into the current production program.

At the time of her death in 1946, Sister Innocentia left a large collectin of drawings and sketches belonging to the Siessen Convent, but only some of these have been made into figurines. A flurry of these designs appeared shortly after the end of World War II. At that time, the U.S. Military Government of Germany, having jurisdiction over the Coburg area, the town of Oeslau, and the Goebel firm, granted W. Goebel permission to manufacture and export "M.I. Hummel" figurines and other collectors' items, which lifted the prewar embargo of 1939.

Master Sculptor Gerhard Skrobek

The town of Oeslau, which today has been annexed into the incorporated community of Rödental, was part of the *Kreis* (county) Coburg and the German state of Thuringia until 1920, when the *Kreis* Coburg was ceded to the free state of Bavaria.

After the great postwar boom of new figurine designs, the next new figurines, six designs, made their debut at the New York World's Fair during 1964 and 1965. The most recent appearance of new "M.I. Hummel" figurines took place at the one-hundredth anniversary of the W. Goebel firm in Rödental, West Germany, in 1971 when four new models were put into production and the first W. Goebel Annual Plate was introduced.

It is important to remember that the approval of a design model by the Siessen Convent does not mean that the particular figurine model will be immediately put into the W. Goebel current production program. When and how many new "M.I. Hummel" figurines are released is a closely guarded company secret.

2 MOLDMAKING

Once the new design is approved for production, the chief designer cuts the original clay model into parts. This is done to facilitate their easy removal from the first molding in plaster of paris—the mother mold, or *Mutterform* in the language of the German porcelain and ceramic trade—and to give the figurines a flow and animation that would be impossible to achieve if they were molded as one piece.

From the mother mold, mother models *(Muttermodellen)*, also of plaster of paris, are created. Craftsmen then carve fine details into these mother models in correspondence with the original clay model. From the mother models, plaster of paris forms *(Modellformen)* are made.

Then, a special acrylic resin *(Kunstharz)* is poured around the plaster of paris model form to create the acrylic working model *(Arbeitsmodell)*. Prior to 1954, these working models were made only of plaster of paris and tended to "grow" slightly. But W. Goebel research, pioneering the acrylic resin process, established a new standard of exactness for achieving uniform figurine size. From these acrylic resin working models, the plaster of paris working molds are formed *(Arbeitsformen)*.

Finally, from the working molds the actual pieces are created.

3 POURING

Liquid ceramic material, referred to in the trade as "slip" is pumped through factory pipelines from the batching room to the molding department, where workers force the slip into the working molds with special injection guns. This slip is a special blend of materials formulated by the W. Goebel ceramic chemists at the factory laboratory to meet the hardness and durability standards required in the manufacture of "M.I. Hummel" figurines.

The composition of this ceramic material includes kaolin from England, feldspar from Norway, clay from the Westerwald region of West Germany, and quartz from both West Germany and Norway. These elements are blended together and milled for about eight hours in huge cylindrical mixers filled with special French and Belgian millstones. After the mixing process, the ceramic material is quality checked and sent through a demagnitizer to make sure that no iron specks find their way into the figurines. Upon reaching the molding department, the material is injected into forms.

Absorbing water from the liquid ceramic material, the working mold leaves a solid ceramic shell on its inner walls. After about twenty minutes, the shell hardens sufficiently, obtains crisp detail, and is removed from the mold by hand. Each mold can be utilized for twenty to twenty-five pourings before water absorption causes so much expansion that it

must be discarded to avoid discrepancies in the accuracy of detail. A fresh plaster of paris mold is then put on the production line. This constant changing of the plaster of paris molds helps to control the uniformity of "M.I. Hummel" figurines.

Prior to 1954 the W. Goebel firm and the porcelain and ceramic industries in general were all making their working models out of plaster of paris. These working models lost their detail very quickly and though they were frequently replaced, the walls of the plaster of paris model expanded about 1 per cent each pouring. As a result, prior to 1954 "M.I. Hummel" figurines sometimes "grew" anywhere between ten and twenty per cent. This accounts for height variations which many collectors have noted on some of their older figurines when comparing them with newer figurines of the same model. The introduction of acrylic resin working models pioneered by W. Goebel research in 1954 eliminated this problem, giving the figurines much more detail while retaining a standard size. This development soon spread through the entire industry.

4 GARNISHING

Once removed from the forms, the parts are put on pallets and sent to the "garnishing" department where they are assembled and aligned to match the original positioning of the Convent-approved model. An "M.I. Hummel" figurine may consist of as many as thirty-nine singly molded parts—as in "Adventure Bound" for example—which are hollow to prevent an explosion caused by the intense heat of the firing process. The hollowness and the production of the figurines in sections has enabled W. Goebel to achieve an elegancy and flow of movement that could never be duplicated if the figurine were poured as one piece. After the garnishing process, the assembled figurine is trimmed of excess ceramic material, dried, quality control checked, and marked with the Goebel registered trademark.

5 FIRING AND GLAZING

Placed on a car lined with refractory bricks, the figurine is then moved slowly through its initial kiln firing in the tunnel oven at a temperature of 2,100° fahrenheit. It is left to cool and then dipped or sprayed with a liquid glazing compound which colors it light blue. The blue color is merely an indicator to help the glazer ensure that the figurine has been totally covered by the glazing bath. The glaze, which is actually a liquified glass, gives a shine to the previously dull bisque figurines. The composition of the glaze allows the figurine to "breathe" during the second firing at 1,870° fahrenheit and combines with the hollow structure to keep it from exploding at the high temperatures. After a quality check, the figurine is put on a pallet and taken to the painting division.

6 PAINTING

The painting of an "M.I. Hummel" figurine is a painstaking process. It is done by teams of artists who have undergone extensive training. In a systematic performance of thoroughly executed phases, the sharp eye of the painter coordinates the design of his figurine with the Convent-approved original. Over 2,000 color variations of ceramic paints are mixed daily for use on the various figurines in production, with master painters presiding over teams of about a dozen artists in bright airy ateliers. Paints are composed of metallic oxides and pulverized glaze with a small amount of oil base added. Iron, cadmium, copper, cobalt, chromium, vanadium, magnesium, and nickel are all used, and when combined with the glaze base and heated for the final firing at 1,407° fahrenheit, they melt into the figurine, giving it a matte finish once again.

From time to time the master painter will paint an initial or a number on the bottom of the figurine base to indicate that he and his team were responsible for the painting. Though this initial or number appears near the trademark, it in no way determines the date of manufacture or size of the model. It is a symbol intended for internal reference.

7 PACKAGING

After the "M.I. Hummel" figurines have been painted and fired for the final time, they are subjected to a last strenuous quality check—much more rigorous than those that take place when a figurine is passed from one department to another. Some figurines are sent back to the painting division for retouching, others are designated as seconds and destroyed. The majority of figurines go on to the packaging department where they are wrapped and placed in "styropor" boxes to eliminate breakage in transit. They are then inventoried and placed in large containers for direct shipment around the world.

TRAINING OF GOEBEL CRAFTSMEN

The legacy of porcelain and ceramic craftsmanship, passed from generation to generation since the days when it was a "cottage industry" prior to the industrial revolution, is a traditional form of artistry that requires not only talent but also patience for those who choose to learn. Nineteenth century Germany, recognizing the importance of specialized training for the porcelain and ceramic trades, was the first European nation to establish a technical academy, at the town of Bunzlau, to foster the art and ensure its perpetuation. A second academy was opened in the 1870s in the Bavarian city of Landshut. The profession of *Porzellaner* (porcelain craftsman) is not only a proud one but also a continuing one, with many German families encouraging their children to continue the trade. The W. Goebel *Porzellanfabrik* follows in this tradition by employing members of these talented families generation after generation.

Before beginning to manufacture "M.I. Hummel" figurines and other collector items, the Goebel firm established its own in-house school, which, in conjunction with the State Academy for Porcelain and Ceramic Arts in the town of Selb, continues to grant the diplomas for *Porzellaner* (porcelain craftsman) and *Porzellanmaler* (porcelain designer). In order to earn their diplomas, all Goebel candidates must complete a rigid three-

year course, a three-faceted program that combines factory training with classroom learning and three months of study each year at the State Academy in Selb.

Hiring by need, the W. Goebel firm strives to attract young students between the ages of seventeen and eighteen who have finished their high school education and are inclined toward the porcelain trade. Carefully screened for interest and ability, all applicants must pass a series of

comprehensive examinations given by the firm. Only the highest scoring applicants are considered. Once accepted into the Goebel program, the future craftsman begins his three-year apprenticeship, dividing his time between the W. Goebel factory, the in-house classroom, and the State Academy at Selb. Students learn drawing, design, moldmaking, and the chemistry of porcelain and ceramics—not only discussing the subjects in theory but

242

also having the opportunity to broaden their knowledge through practical application as well. At the end of the three-year program, the student receives a diploma and is assigned to the particular branch of the factory for which he has demonstrated the greatest aptitude and talent.

With all the social benefits available at W. Goebel, work is a teamlike, almost familial experience. This spirit, combined with the outstanding leadership of the W. Goebel firm in the labor relations field, provides a nearly perfect working environment where craftsmen often spend thirty to forty years working at their trades, teaching and ensuring a younger generation that the great porcelain tradition of Bavaria and Thuringia will be carried on.

W. GOEBEL
FIRM HISTORY
THE TRADITION
OF THE
COBURG-RÖDENTAL
AREA

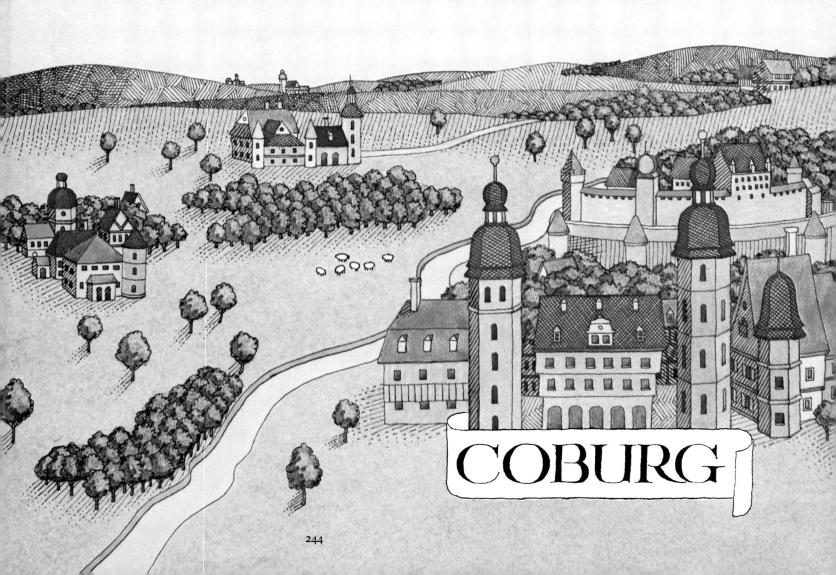

COBURG

Inscriptions like this one denote the historic landmarks of the area.

The W. Goebel factory circa 1928.

On a nice day, W. Goebel workers often find it relaxing to take a leisurely lunch hour stroll.

The W. Goebel firm stems from a long tradition in porcelain and ceramics that began near the city of Coburg, Germany, over two centuries ago. During the mid-1750s, high-quality clay and sand were discovered in the village of Einberg, near Coburg, and in 1765 Johann Wolfgang Hammann founded the first porcelain factory in the state of Thuringia. Hammann's factory, in the town of Wallendorf, near the clay and sand deposits of Einberg, was known as the Wallendorf Works. Hammann's daughter, Christiana Catherina, married the artist Friedrich Christian Hutschenreuther of Wallendorf, and their granddaughter, Aline Hutschenreuther, married Franz-Detleff Goebel of nearby Reichmannsdorf.

In 1853, nearly twenty years before he was granted royal permission by the Dukes of Saxe-Coburg-Gotha to go into the porcelain business, Franz-Detleff Goebel applied to the local Coburg government for a permit to build a porcelain kiln. Answerable to the powerful Dukes of Saxe-Coburg-Gotha, the local government acted in fear of its royal leaders and informed Franz-Detleff that the construction of a porcelain kiln in Coburg would present a serious fire hazard.

Finally, on January 20, 1871, Franz-Detleff Goebel and his son William were granted permission to manufacture what was then known as Thuringer Ware, namely blackboards, slate, pencils, and children's shooting marbles. But Franz-Detleff would not stand to manufacture simply these goods. In 1879 he took his case directly to Duke Ernst II of Saxe-Coburg-Gotha to protest the delay. Shortly thereafter, in a surprising decision, Duke Ernst II gave his permission for Franz-Detleff Goebel to build a porcelain kiln outside the city of Coburg in the village of Oeslau, only two miles from the rich clay and sand deposits at Einberg and Kipfendorf. In the same year, the F. & W. Goebel Porcelain Works began manufacturing their first kiln-fired products, items for daily use such as dinner services, milk pitchers, beer steins, and egg cups. Franz-Detleff Goebel had shown the local Coburg government what kind of wood he was hewn from.

At the turn of the century, after Franz-Detleff had died, his son William developed the firm's manufacture of porcelain dinnerware and figurines into an export-oriented business. Upon William's death in 1912, his son Max-Louis took over the business, and by 1914 the firm employed 400 workers.

A productive, innovative personality, Max-Louis Goebel influenced product design by inaugurating his own concepts and art forms. He surprised his customers with so many new porcelain figurine designs that he earned the name "novelty Goebel." His greatest innovation came in 1926 when he implemented the production of ceramic figurines to complement the porcelain line. Priced competitively, the ceramics sold increasingly well and other firms began to imitate his style. A decade later the breadth of this ceramic undertaking gave birth to "M.I. Hummel" figurines.

Max-Louis died in 1929. His son Franz assumed directorship of the firm along with his mother, Frieda, and his brother-in-law, Dr. Eugen Stocke. The trio, under the leadership of Franz Goebel, immediately began efforts to bring the firm out of the effects of the postwar economic depression and the resulting inflationary spiral. With the debut of "M.I. Hummel" figurines in 1935, the firm made a dramatic upsurge from the hard times that followed the First World War. But with the specter of Nazism hanging over Europe and the resulting wartime embargo of German goods, production slowed considerably. During the Second World War the firm concentrated on the manufacture of dinnerware for the domestic market, though some figurines were produced.

Just a few minutes from the factory, the renovated Schloss Neuhof (Neuhof Castle) is an example of traditional architecture. The Schloss now serves as a hotel/restaurant, with one of the largest private bird parks in Europe.

A stylized W. Goebel trademark in ornamental iron, adorns a factory portico.

Approaching a modern wing of the factory, one begins to feel the harmonious mix of tradition, old and new.

Summer colors brighten Coburg's traditional Saturday market.

Under the leadership of Franz Goebel, together with Dr. Eugen Stocke, the firm made a rapid recovery after the Second World War, largely because the U.S. Military Government of Germany quickly lifted the wartime embargo and gave permission for the production and exportation of "M.I. Hummel" figurines and other objects in 1946. U.S. occupation forces in Germany and European tourists comprised another important market for figurine sales, and by 1951—two years after the creation of the Federal Republic of Germany—the W. Goebel firm employed 700 workers.

By the late 1960s the great *Wirtschaftswunder* (economic miracle) of postwar West Germany had taken place, and W. Goebel, like many export-oriented German firms, had achieved great success. The firm was employing 1,400 craftsmen in the manufacture of "M.I. Hummel" figurines and other objects. Franz Goebel, who as a young man had lived in France, Canada, and the United States, continued to rely on his strong ability to judge the export market, leading his firm into an era of diversification and expansion.

In 1956 Goebel started a subsidiary in the United States. He also opened a toy and doll factory as a subsidiary in 1957, where the "M.I. Hummel" dolls are made. The *Oeslauer Porzellan Manufaktur*, later renamed *Oeslauer Manufaktur*,

Taking a break.

The Loreley, Coburg's oldest and most famous inn.

was founded in 1968 and produces high-quality porcelain dinnerware for both home and export markets. Shortly before his sixty-fifth birthday celebration in July 1969, Franz Goebel died. Franz Goebel's son, Wilhelm, and Ulrich Stocke, son of Dr. Eugen Stocke, took on the leadership of the firm with Dr. Stocke as mentor. This fifth generation took over the subsidiary enterprises as well.

Carrying on in the tradition established over one hundred years ago, Wilhelm Goebel and Ulrich Stocke have brought young and dynamic leadership to the Goebel concept. In the words of the current leadership, they are striving to achieve a second century "obligated to the past, dedicated to the present, open to the future."

The relationship among the directors, managers, craftsmen, and workmen is brought closer together through social and recreational activities. They have built a company sauna, a heated outdoor swimming pool, tennis courts, a library, and a day-care center for the young children of their employees. In keeping with this spirit, both the Goebel and Stocke families take an active interest in community cultural life and sports. Wilhelm Goebel and Ulrich Stocke make frequent visits to the production areas to discuss technical and job-related problems, and often take active parts in the factorywide employee meetings as well.

W. Goebel has continued to acquire new firms with great traditions of craftsmanship, thus sustaining the trend toward expansion established by Franz Goebel before his untimely death. In 1971, the Meudt Pottery Works was founded by W. Goebel for the manufacture of ceramic lamps and other items.

The ancient art of salt-glazed stoneware manufacture was kept alive in 1972 when W. Goebel acquired co-ownership in the Merkelbach *Manufaktur* of Höhr-Grenzhausen, near Cologne, whose blue and gray beer steins, mugs, and wine pitchers have been world renowned for over two centuries. In the same year they acquired the Charlottenhütte Glass and Crystal *Manufaktur* in Werdohl, where the difficult and ancient craft of hand blowing glass is still continued.

W. Goebel has become a modern, diversified firm by combining the creative planning of its leadership with the time honored skills of its craftsmen to win a place for its Bavarian and Thuringian handcrafted art objects on the market. The fact that "M.I. Hummel" figurines are sold in over eighty countries proves that the W. Goebel *Porzellanfabrik* and Sister Maria Innocentia Hummel's "Merry Wanderer" have taken a bit of Bavarian *gemütlichkeit* around the world.

The view atop the fortressed walls of Veste Coburg (Coburg Castle) glances down on the entire county.

Young children of W. Goebel employees spend their days playfully at the company's own kindergarten.

The long factory buildings run back from the main road for nearly half a mile.

INDEX:

Alphabetical Listing of all "M.I. Hummel" art objects.
A valuable cross-reference to use alone or in conjunction with
the numerical listing appearing on page 38

NAME	HUM No.
A Fair Measure/*Der Kaufmann*	345
Accordion Boy/*Bandoneonspieler*	185
Adoration/*Bei Mutter Maria, Marterl*	23
Adoration with Bird/*Bei Mutter Maria, Marterl, mit Vogel*	105
Adventure Bound, The Seven Swabians/*Die Sieben Schwaben*	347
Angel Duet/*Stille Nacht, ohne Kerzentülle*	261
Angel Serenade/*Fromme Weisen* [With Lamb]	83
Angel Serenade/*Fromme Weisen, kniender Engel*	214D
Angel with accordion/*Engel mit Bandoneon*	238B
Angel with lute/*Engel mit Laute*	238A
Angel with Trumpet/*Engel mit Trompete*	238C
Angelic Song/*Singendes Kind mit Engelein*	144
Apple Tree Boy/*Herbst, Junge im Baum*	142
Apple Tree Girl/*Frühling, Mädchen im Baum*	141
Arithmetic Lesson/*Rechenstunde* [School Lesson]	303
Art Critic/*Der Kunstkritiker*	318
At the Fence/*Am Zaun* [The Other Side of the Fence]	324
Auf Wiedersehen/*Auf Wiedersehen, Kinderpaar*	153
Autumn Harvest/*Herbstsegen*	355
Baker/*Der kleine Konditor*	128
Baking Day/*Die Bäckerin* [Kneading Dough]	330
Band Leader/*Herr Kapellmeister*	129
Barnyard Hero/*Angsthase*	195
Bashful!/*Vergissmeinnicht*	377
Begging his Share/*Gratulant*	9
Behave!/*Wir gehen spazieren* [Walking Her Dog]	339
Be Patient/*Entenmütterchen*	197
Being Punished/*Junge im Karzer* [Naughty Boy]	326
Big Housecleaning/*Grossreinemachen*	363
Bird Duet/*Frühlingslied*	169
Bird Watcher/*Der Tierfreund*	300
Birthday Cake/*Der Geburtstagskuchen* [A Birthday Wish] [Candle Holder]	338
Birthday Present/*Das Geburtstagsgeschenk*	341
Birthday Serenade/*Geburtstagsständchen*	218
Blessed Event/*Das grosse Ereignis*	333
Book Worm/*Der Bücherwurm*	3
Book Worm/*Der Bücherwurm*	8
Boots/*Meister Wichtig*	143
Boy with Accordion/*Junge mit Bandoneon*	390
Boy with Horse/*Junge mit Holzpferd*	239C
Boy with Toothache/*Schmerz lass nach*	217
Brother/*Dorfheld*	95
Busy Student/*Musterschülerin*	367
Candlelight/*Engel mit Kerze* [Candle Holder]	192
Carnival/*Fastnacht*	328
Celestian Musician/*Himmlische Klänge*	188
Chick Girl/*Kükenmütterchen*	57

NAME	HUM No.
Chicken-Licken!/*Kükenliesl*	385
Chimney Sweep/*Ich bringe Glück, Kaminfeger*	12
Christ Child/*Stille Nacht, Jesuskind*	18
Christmas Angel/*Der Weihnachtsengel* [Delivery Angel]	301
Christmas Song/*Weihnachtslied* [Singing Angel]	343
Cinderella/*Aschenputtel*	337
Close Harmony/*Geburtstagsständchen*	336
Companions/*Gratulanten-Muttertag* [Brotherly Love]	370
Concentration/*Wie macht sie das nur?* [Knit One, Purl Two]	302
Confidentially/*Zwiegespräch*	314
Congratulations/*Ich gratuliere*	17
Crossroads/*Am Scheideweg*	331
Culprits/*Apfeldieb, Junge*	56A
Coquettes/*Zaungäste*	179
Daddy's Girls/*Gratulanten-Vatertag* [Sisterly Love]	371
Daisies Don't Tell/*Er liebt mich* [Does He?]	380
Doctor/*Puppendoktor*	127
Doll Bath/*Puppenbad*	319
Doll Mother/*Puppenmütterchen*	67
Don't be Shy/*Da nimm's doch* [One For You—One For Me]	379
Duet/*Duett, Sängerpaar*	130
Easter Greetings!/*Ostergruss*	378
Easter Time/*Osterfreude* [Easter Playmates]	384
Eventide/*Abendlied*	99
Farewell/*Auf Wiedersehen*	65
Farm Boy/*Schweinehirt*	66
Favorite Pet/*Ostergruss*	361
Feathered Friends/*Schwanenteich*	344
Feeding Time/*Im Hühnerhof*	199
Festival Harmony (Flute)/*Adventsengel mit Flöte*	173
Festival Harmony (Mandolin)/*Adventsengel mit Mandoline*	172
Flower Madonna/*Blumen-Madonna mit Kind*	10
Flower Vendor/*Zum Blumenmarkt*	381
Follow the Leader/*Mach mit*	369
Forest Shrine/*Waldandacht, Marterl*	183
For Father/*Fürs Vaterle, Rettichbub*	87
Friends/*Gute Freunde*	136
Gay Adventure/*Frohes Wandern*	356
Girl with doll/*Mädchen mit Puppe*	239B
Girl with nosegay/*Mädchen mit Blumenstrauss*	239A
Girl with sheet of music/*Mädchen mit Notenblatt*	389
Girl with trumpet/*Mädchen mit Trompete*	391
Globe Trotter/*Hinaus in die Ferne*	79
Going Home/*Wanderfreunde* [Fancy Free]	383
Going to Grandma's/*Hausmütterchen*	52
Good Friends/*Mädchen mit Böckchen*	182
Good Hunting!/*Weidmannsheil!*	307
Good Shepherd/*Der gute Hirte*	42
Goose Girl/*Gänseliesl*	47
Guiding Angel/*Kniender Engel mit Laterne*	357
Happiness/*Wanderlied, Mädchen*	86
Happy Birthday/*Gratulanten*	176
Happy Days/*Hausmusik, Kinderpaar*	150
Happy Pastime/*Strickliesl*	69
Happy Traveller/*Hinaus in die Ferne*	109
Hear Ye, Hear Ye/*Hört Ihr Leute, Nachtwächter*	15
Heavenly Angel/*Christkindlein kommt, Engel*	21
Heavenly Lullaby/*Wiegenlied, ohne Kerzentülle*	262
Heavenly Protection/*Schutzengel*	88
Heavenly Song/*Stille Nacht, Adventsgruppe* [Candle Holder]	113

NAME	HUM No.
Hello/*Chef*	124
Helping Mother/*Mutters grosse Stütze* [Mother's Aid]	325
Home from Market/*Glück auf, Junge mit Schweinchen*	198
Homeward Bound/*Heimkehr vom Felde*	334
Honey Lover/*Honiglecker* [In the Jam Pot]	312
I Forgot/*Ich hab's vergessen* [Thoughtful]	362
Infant of Krumbad/*Jesuskind, liegend*	78
Joyous News/*O, du fröhliche*	27
Joyful/*Gesangsprobe*	53
Just Fishing/*Der Fischer* [The Fisherman]	373
Just Resting/*Mutters Liebste*	112
Kiss Me!/*Hab' mich lieb!*	311
Knitting Lesson/*Ob's gelingt?*	256
Latest News/*Das Allerneueste*	184
Letter to Santa Claus/*Brief ans Christkind*	340
Let's Sing/*Heini, Bandoneonspieler*	110
Little Band/*Kindergruppe*	392
Little Bookkeeper/*Stellvertretung*	306
Little Cellist/*Heimkehr, Bassgeiger*	89
Little Drummer/*Trommler*	240
Little Fiddler/*Geigerlein ohne Hund*	2
Little Fiddler/*Geigerlein ohne Hund*	4
Little Gabriel/*O, du fröhliche…, Engel*	32
Little Gardener/*Die kleine Gärtnerin*	74
Little Goat Herder/*Ziegenbub*	200
Little Guardian/*Betendes Kind mit Engelein*	145
Little Helper/*Fleissiges Lieschen*	73
Little Hiker/*Hans im Glück*	16
Little Nurse/*"Hänsel, merk dir das"* [First Aid]	376
Little Pharmacist/*Der Apotheker*	322
Little Scholar/*Erster Schulgang, Junge*	80
Little Shopper/*Gretel*	96
Little Sweeper/*Kehrliesl*	171
Little Tailor/*Schneiderlein*	308
Little Thrifty/*Spar-Hummelchen*	118
Little Velma/*Die kleine Velma*	219
Littlest Angel/*'s Hummele* [The Wee Angel]	365
Lost Sheep/*Schäferbub*	68
Lost Stocking/*Hab mein Strumpf verloren*	374
Lucky Boy/*Der Glücksbub* [Fair Prizes]	335
Lute Song/*Lautenspiel* [Lute Player]	368
Madonna/*Sitzende Madonna mit sitzendem Kind*	151
Madonna with halo/*Madonna mit Heiligenschein*	45
Madonna without halo/*Madonna ohne Heiligenschein*	46
March Winds/*Lausbub*	43
Max and Moritz/*Max und Moritz*	123
Meditation/*Die Gratulantin*	13
Merry Wanderer/*Wanderbub ohne Hund*	7
Merry Wanderer/*Wanderbub ohne Hund*	11
Mischief Maker/*Der Störenfried*	342
Morning Stroll/*Ausfahrt* [Walking the Baby]	375
For Mother/*Fürs Mütterchen*	257
Mother's Darling/*Markt-Christel*	175
Mother's Helper/*Mutters Stütze*	133
Mountaineer/*I hab's erreicht*	315
Not for you!/*Nix für dich!*	317
Off to School/*Frisch gewagt* [Kindergarten Romance]	329
Old Man Reading Newspaper/*Opa liest die Zeitung*	181
Old Man to Market/*Opa geht auf den Markt*	191
Old Woman Knitting/*Die alte Strickerin*	189
Old Woman to Market/*Oma geht auf den Markt*	190
On Holiday/*Zum Festtag* [Holiday Shopper]	350

NAME	HUM No.
On Secret Path/*Auf heimlichen Wegen*	386
Out of Danger/*In Sicherheit, Mädchen*	56B
Photographer/*Der Fotograf*	178
Playmates/*Hasenvater*	58
Postman/*Eilbote*	119
Prayer before Battle/*Der fromme Reitersmann*	20
Puppy Love/*Geigerlein mit Hund*	1
Relaxation/*Eine gute Erholung* [Nightly Ritual]	316
Retreat to Safety/*In tausend Ängsten*	201
Ride into Christmas/*Fahrt in die Weihnacht*	396
School Boy/*Schulschwänzer*	82
School Boys/*Schwieriges Problem*	170
School Girl/*Erster Schulgang*	81
School Girls/*'s Meisterstück*	177
Saint George/*Ritter Heiliger Georg*	55
Sensitive Hunter/*Jägerlein*	6
Serenade/*Ständchen, Junge mit Flöte*	85
She loves me, she loves me not!/*Liebt mich, liebt mich nicht*	174
Shepherd Boy/*Hirtenbub* [Young Shepherd]	395
Shepherd's Boy/*Schäferbub*	64
Shining Light/*Kniender Engel mit Kerze*	358
Signs of Spring/*Frühlingsidyll*	203
Singing Lesson/*'s stimmt net*	63
Sister/*Der erste Einkauf*	98
Skier/*Ski-Heil*	59
Smart little Sister/*Das kleine Schwesterlein*	346
Soldier Boy/*Still gestanden!*	332
Soloist/*Heldentenor*	135
Spring Cheer/*Frühling ist's*	72
Spring Dance/*Sommertanz*	353
Star Gazer/*Sterngucker*	132
Stitch in time/*Zwei rechts—zwei links*	255
Stormy Weather/*Unter einem Dach*	71
Street Singer/*Kammersänger*	131
Strolling Along/*Wanderbub mit Hund*	5
Sunny Morning/*Sonnenkind* [Slumber Serenade]	313
Surprise/*Hänsel und Gretel*	94
Sweet Greetings/*Ein süsser Gruss* [Musical Good Morning]	352
Sweet Music/*Zum Tanz, Bassgeiger*	186
Telling Her Secret/*Das Geheimnis*	196
The Artist/*Kunstmaler*	304
The Botanist/*Enzian-Mädchen* [Remembering]	351
The Builder/*Schwerarbeiter*	305
The Florist/*Der Blumenfreund* [Flower Lover]	349
The Holy Child/*Jesulein*	70
The mail is here/*Trara- die Post ist da*	226
The Professor/*Der Professor*	320
The Run-a-way/*Der frohe Wanderer*	327
Timid Little Sister/*Das ängstliche Schwesterlein*	394
To Market/*Brüderlein und Schwesterlein*	49
Trumpet Boy/*Der kleine Musikant*	97
Tuneful Angel/*Kniender Engel mit Horn*	359
Umbrella Boy/*Geborgen, Junge*	152A
Umbrella Girl/*Geborgen, Mädchen*	152B
Valentine Gift/*Valentinsgeschenk, "I hab di gern"*	387
Village Boy/*Dorfbub*	51
Visiting an Invalid/*Krankenbesuch*	382
Volunteers/*Soldatenspiel*	50
Waiter/*Herr Ober*	154
Wash Day/*Grosse Wäsche*	321
Watchful Angel/*Schutzengel* [Angelic Care]	194
Wayside Devotion/*Abendlied, Marterl*	28

NAME	HUM No.

Wayside Harmony/*Vaters G'scheitester* — 111
Weary Wanderer/*In Lauterbach hab i...* — 204
We Congratulate/*Pärchen* — 220
Which Hand?/*Rat mal!* — 258
Whitsuntide/*Glockenturm mit Engeln* — 163
With Loving Greetings/*Ein dicker Gruss* [Greetings From] — 309
Worship/*Am Wegesrand, Bildstöckl* — 84

ANNIVERSARY PLATES/*JUBILÄUMSTELLER*

1975, Stormy Weather/*Unter einem Dach* — 280
1980, Pair of girls from Ring Around the Rosie/*2 Mädchen aus Ringelreihen* — 281

ANNUAL BELLS/*JAHRESGLOCKEN*

Annual Bell 1978, Let's Sing/*Jahresglocke 1978, Heini, Bandoneonspieler* — 700
Annual Bell 1979, Farewell/*Jahresglocke 1979, Auf Wiedersehen* — 701

ANNUAL PLATES/*JAHRESTELLER*

Annual plate 1971, Heavenly Angel/*Jahresteller 1971, Christkindlein Kommt, Engel* — 264
Annual plate 1972, Hear Ye, Hear Ye/*Jahresteller 1972, Hört Ihr Leute, Nachtwächter* — 265
Annual plate 1973, Globe Trotter/*Jahresteller 1973, Hinaus in die Ferne* — 266
Annual plate 1974, Goose Girl/*Jahresteller 1974, Gänseliesl* — 267
Annual plate 1975, Ride into Christmas/*Jahresteller 1975, Fahrt in die Weihnacht* — 268
Annual plate 1976, Apple Tree Girl/*Jahresteller 1976, Frühling, Mädchen im Baum* — 269
Annual plate 1977, Apple Tree Boy/*Jahresteller 1977, Herbst, Junge im Baum* — 270
Annual plate 1978, Happy Pastime/*Jahresteller 1978, Strickliesl* — 271
Annual plate 1979, Singing Lesson/*Jahresteller 1979, 's stimmt net* — 272
Annual plate 1980, School Girl/*Jahresteller 1980, Erster Schulgang* — 273
Annual plate 1981, Umbrella Boy/*Jahresteller 1981, Geborgen, Junge* — 274
Annual plate 1982, Umbrella Girl/*Jahresteller 1982, Geborgen, Mädchen* — 275
Annual plate 1983, Postman/*Jahresteller 1983, Eilbote* — 276
Annual plate 1984, Little Helper/*Jahresteller 1984, Fleissiges Lieschen* — 277
Annual plate 1985, Chick Girl/*Jahresteller 1985, Kükenmütterchen* — 278
Annual plate 1986, Playmates/*Jahresteller 1986, Hasenvater* — 279

ASHTRAYS/*ASCHER*

Boy with bird/*Junge mit Vogel* — 166
Happy Pastime/*Strickliesl* — 62
Joyful/*Gesangsprobe* — 33
Joyful (without rest for cigarette)/*Gesangsprobe (ohne Zigarettenablage)* — 216 **(CN)**
Let's Sing/*Heini, Bandoneonspieler* — 114
Singing Lesson/*'s stimmt net* — 34

BOOK ENDS/*BUCHSTÜTZEN*

Apple Tree Girl & Apple Tree Boy/*Frühling, Mädchen im Baum und Herbst, Junge im Baum* — 252A & B
Book Worm, Boy and Girl/*Der Bücherwurm, Junge und Mädchen* — 14A + B
Doll Mother & Prayer before Battle/*Puppenmütterchen und Der fromme Reitersmann* — 76A + B
Eventide & Adoration (without shrine)/*Abendlied und Bei Mutter Maria (ohne Marterl)* — 90A + B
Farm Boy & Goose Girl/*Schweinehirt und Gänseliesl* — 60A + B
Good Friends & She loves me, she loves me not!/*Freunde und Lieb mich, liebt mich nicht!* — 251A + B
Joyful and Let's Sing/*Gesangsprobe und Heini, Bandoneonspieler* — 120
Little Goat Herder & Feeding Time/*Ziegenbub und Im Hühnerhof* — 250A + B

NAME	HUM No.

Playmates & Chick Girl/*Hasenvater und Kükenmütterchen* — 61A + B
Puppy Love and Serenade with dog/*Geigerlein und Ständchen, mit Hund* — 122
Wayside Harmony and Just Resting/*Vaters G'scheitester und Mutters Liebste* — 121

CANDLE HOLDERS/*LEUCHTER*

NAME	HUM No.
Angel Duet/*Stille Nacht, Engelgrüppchen*	193
Angel Lights/*Engelbrücke*	241
Angelic Sleep/*Stille Nacht*	25
Begging his Share (Before 1964)/*Gratulant*	9
Birthday Cake/*Der Geburtstagskuchen* [A Birthday Wish]	338
Boy with horse/*Adventsleuchter, Junge mit Holzpferd*	117
Candlelight/*Engel mit Kerze*	192
Girl with fir tree/*Adventsleuchter, Mädchen mit Tannenbaum*	116
Girl with nosegay/*Adventsleuchter, Mädchen mit Blumenstrauss*	115
Heavenly Song/*Stille Nacht, Adventsgruppe*	113
Herald Angels/*Adventsleuchter mit drei Engeln*	37
Joyous News/*O, du fröhliche*	27/I
Joyous News, Angel with Accordion/*Adventsengelchen mit Bandoneon*	39
Joyous News, Angel with Lute/*Adventsengelchen mit Laute*	38
Joyous News, Angel with Trumpet/*Adventsengelchen mit Trompete*	40
Little Band/*Kindergruppe*	388
Lullaby/*Wiegenlied*	24
Silent Night/*Stille Nacht, Krippe*	54
Silent Night with Black Child/*Stille Nacht, Krippe mit schwarzem Kindlein*	31

CANDY BOXES/*DOSEN*

NAME	HUM No.
Chick Girl/*Kükenmütterchen*	III/57
Happy Pastime/*Strickliesl*	III/69
Happy Pastime, old style/*Strickliesl, alter Stil*	221**(CN)**
Joyful/*Gesangsprobe*	III/53
Let's Sing/*Heini, Bandoneonspieler*	III/110
Playmates/*Hasenvater*	III/58
Singing Lesson/*'s stimmt net*	III/63

HOLY WATER FONTS/*WEIHKESSEL*

NAME	HUM No.
Angel Cloud/*Kind auf Wolke*	206
Angel Duet/*Engelgrüppchen*	146
Angel, Joyous News/*Adventsengelchen*	242
Angel looking left/*Engel linksschauend*	91A
Angel looking right/*Engel rechtsschauend*	91B
Angel Shrine/*Engel*	147
Angel with Bird/*Sitzender Engel mit Vogel*	167
Angel with Cross and Bird/*Engel mit Kreuz und Vogel*	354C
Angel with Lantern/*Engel mit Laterne, Weihkessel*	354A
Angel with Lute/*Engel mit Laute*	241
Angel with Trumpet/*Engel mit Trompete*	354B
Child Jesus/*Christkindlein*	26
Child with Flowers/*Kind mit Blumen*	36
Dove Font/*Taube Weihkessel*	393
Guardian Angel/*Schutzengel*	29
Guardian Angel/*Schutzengel*	248
Heavenly Angel/*Christkindlein kommt, Engel*	207
Holy Cross/*Heiliges Kreuz*	77
Holy Family/*Heilige Familie*	246
Madonna and Child/*Madonna und Kind*	243
Sitting Angel/*Sitzender Engel*	22
The Good Shepherd/*Der gute Hirte*	35
White Angel/*Weisser Engel*	75
Worship/*Am Wegesrand*	164

NAME	HUM No.

MUSIC BOXES/*MUSIKWERKE*

Little Band on Music Box/*Kindergruppe mit Musikwerk*	392M
Little Band, Candlestick on Music Box/*Leuchter, Kindergruppe auf Musikdose*	388M

NATIVITY SETS/*KRIPPENSÄTZE*

Large nativity set with wooden stable/*Krippensatz, gross mit Holzstall*	260

Components:/*Komponenten:*

Angel Serenade/*Fromme Weisen*	260E
Cow, lying/*Liegende Kuh*	260M
Donkey, standing/*Stehender Esel*	260L
Good Night/*Angenehme Ruhe*	260D
Infant Jesus/*Jesuskind*	260C
King, kneeling/*Kniender König*	260P
King, standing/*Stehender König*	260O
Little Tooter/*Schäferbub*	260K
Madonna/*Madonna*	260A
Moorish King, standing/*Stehender Mohrenkönig*	260N
One Sheep, lying/*Liegendes Schaf*	260R
Saint Joseph/*Heiliger Josef*	260B
Sheep standing with lamb/*Stehendes Schaf mit Lamm*	260H
Shepherd Boy, kneeling/*Kniender Hirtenbub*	260J
Shepherd, standing/*Stehender Hirt*	260G
We Congratulate/*Wir gratulieren*	260F

NATIVITY SETS/*KRIPPENSÄTZE*

Nativity set with wooden stable/*Krippensatz mit Holzstall*	214

Components/*Komponenten:*

Angel kneeling, "Angel Serenade"/*Kniender Engel, Fromme Weisen*	214D
Angel, standing "Good Night"/*Stehender Engel, Angenehme Ruhe*	214C
Donkey/*Esel*	214J
Infant Jesus/*Jesuskind*	214A
Joseph/*Josef*	214B
King, kneeling/*Kniender König*	214M
King, kneeling, with cash-box/*Kniender König mit Schatulle*	214N
Lamb/*Lamm*	214O
Moorish King/*Mohrenkönig*	214L
Ox/*Ochse*	214K
Shepherd, kneeling/*Kniender Hirtenbub*	214G
Shepherd, kneeling with flute, "Little Tooter"/*Kniender Hirt mit Flöte, Schäferbub*	214H
Shepherd, standing/*Stehender Hirt*	214F
Virgin Mary/*Heilige Jungfrau*	214A
"We Congratulate"/*Wir gratulieren*	214E

PLAQUES/*WANDBILDER*

Ba-Bee Ring/*Hui, die Hummel, Wandring*	30A + B
Being Punished/*Junge im Karzer* (Naughty Boy)	326
Child in Bed, Wall Plaque/*Kind im Bettchen, Wandring*	137
Flitting Butterfly/*Sitzendes Kind mit Schmetterling*	139
Little Fiddler/*Geigerlein*	93
Little Fiddler (Wood Frame)/*Geigerlein (Holzrahmen)*	107
Madonna and Child (in relief)/*Madonna und Kind (Relief)*	249
Madonna Plaque/*Madonnenbild*	48
Madonna Plaque (Metal Frame)/*Madonnenbild (Metallrahmen)*	222
Merry Christmas/*Frohe Weihnachten*	323
Merry Wanderer/*Wanderbub*	92
Merry Wanderer (Wood Frame)/*Wanderbub (Holzrahmen)*	106
Merry Wanderer (in relief)/*Wanderbub (Relief)*	263

NAME	HUM No.

M.I. Hummel Store Plaque (in English)/*M.I. Hummel Reklame-Schild (auf Englisch)* — 187

M.I. Hummel Display Plaque (redesigned from older model) *Hummel Reklame-Schild (neues Modell)* — 187A

M.I. Hummel Store Plaque (Schmid)/*M.I. Hummel Reklame-Schild (Schmid)* — 210

M.I. Hummel Store Plaque (in English, Oeslau)/*M.I. Hummel Relame-Schild (auf Englisch, Oeslau)* — 211

M.I. Hummel Store Plaque (in French)/*M.I. Hummel Reklame-Schild (auf Französich)* — 208

M.I. Hummel Store Plaque (in German)/*M.I. Hummel Reklame-Schild (auf Deutsch)* — 205

M.I. Hummel Store Plaque (in Spanish)/*M.I. Hummel Reklame-Schild (auf Spanisch)* — 213

M.I. Hummel Store Plaque (in Swedish)/*M.I. Hummel Reklame-Schild (auf Schwedisch)* — 209

Quartet/*Das Quartett* — 134

Retreat to Safety/*Angsthase* — 126

Searching Angel/*Was ist denn da drunten los?* — 310

Smiling Through, Goebel Collectors' Club Plaque/*Immer froh, Bild* — 690

Standing Boy/*Stehender Junge mit Herz und Flasche* — 168

Star Gazer/*Sterngucker* — 237

Swaying Lullaby/*Kind mit Hängematte und Vögeln* — 165

The mail is here/*Trara-die Post ist da* — 140

Tiny Baby in Crib/*Kindlein in Krippe* — 138

Tuneful Goodnight/*Wandschmuck in Herzform, sitzendes Kind mit Trompete* (Happy Bugler) — 180

Vacation-Time/*Ferienfreude* — 125

Wall picture with sitting woman and child/*Wandbild mit sitzender Frau und Kind* — 156

TABLE LAMPS/*LAMPENFÜSSE*

NAME	HUM No.
Apple Tree Boy/*Herbst, Junge im Baum*	230
Apple Tree Girl/*Frühling, Mädchen im Baum*	229
Birthday Serenade/*Geburtstagsständchen*	231
Birthday Serenade/*Geburtstagsständchen*	234
Culprits/*Apfeldieb, Junge*	44A
Farewell/*Auf Wiedersehen*	103
Good Friends/*Mädchen mit Böckchen*	228
Happy Days/*Hausmusik, Kinderpaar*	232
Happy Days/*Hausmusik, Kinderpaar*	235
Just Resting/*Mutters Liebste*	225
Just Resting/*Mutters Liebste*	II/112
Out of Danger/*In Sicherheit, Mädchen*	44B
She loves me, she loves me not.../*Liebt mich, liebt mich nicht*	227
Shrine/*Marterl*	100
To Market/*Brüderlein und Schwesterlein*	223
To Market/*Brüderlein und Schwesterlein*	101
Volunteers/*Soldatenspiel*	102
Wayside Devotion/*Abendlied, Marterl*	104
Wayside Harmony/*Vaters G'scheitester*	224
Wayside Harmony/*Vaters G'scheitester*	II/111

WALL VASES/*WANDVASEN*

NAME	HUM No.
Boy and Girl/*Junge und Mädchen*	360A
Boy/*Junge*	360B
Girl/*Mädchen*	360C